Meet the Presidents!

by Gare Thompson

Scholastic Inc.

WINNING THE WHITE HOUSE

Would you like to be president of the United States someday?
To run for president, you must:

- be at least thirty-five years old
- be a native-born citizen
- have lived in the United States for at least fourteen years

If you meet those qualifications, you can run!

Ready to meet the presidents?

This book is packed with amazing firsts
and cool facts about every U.S. president.
And you can use the sticker sheet to create
a winner's page for this year's presidential
election. Who will win?

Term: 1789–1797
First Lady:
   Martha Washington

Family Man

- One of Washington's nicknames is Father of His Country. Washington had no biological children of his own.
- He adopted his wife's two children from a previous marriage.
- There were about 3,900,000 people in the country when Washington was president, so in a sense, he had a huge family!

Washington's Look

- Washington was tall, about six feet, two inches.
- He had false teeth made from whalebone and ivory— no wooden teeth.
- He wore size 13 shoes. The next presidents had big shoes to fill!

George by the Numbers

1 George has one state named after him.

7 Number of mountains named after George.

10 Number of lakes named after George.

33 Number of counties named after him.

121 Number of towns and villages named after him.

Washington Monument

FAST FACT

Washington had his horses' teeth cleaned each day before he rode them.

Campaign Corner

Washington never campaigned for president. He was unanimously elected for two terms.

Term: 1797–1801
First Lady:
Abigail Adams

Family Man

- Adams's wife, Abigail, and his son John Quincy were famous, too.
- Abigail wrote the famous line to John, "Remember the ladies." She wanted women to have equal rights. But women didn't get the vote until 1920.
- John Quincy later became president. They were the first father and son pair to be presidents.

Nicknames

- As he grew older, Adams gained weight. Some people called him His Rotundity.
- He also started the U.S. Navy, so he was called the Father of the Navy. He liked that nickname better.

Frenemies

Adams became good friends with Thomas Jefferson when they first met in 1775. However, once Adams was president and Jefferson was his vice president, they did not get along. After both retired from politics, they became friends again. Both men died on July 4, 1826, within hours of each other. They were good friends to the end.

Dear Thomas,

The USS *Constitution*

FAST FACT

Adams was the first president to live in the White House. Abigail hung laundry in the East Room.

Campaign Corner

Adams was the first president to run for the office. He beat Thomas Jefferson.

Thomas JEFFERSON

MEET JEFFERSON

Term: 1801–1809
First Lady:
Martha Jefferson
(She died before he became president.)

Animal Lover

Jefferson loved animals. He kept a pet mockingbird named Dick at the White House. He had two grizzly bears (in cages) that lived on the White House lawn. He also kept peacocks and partridges. Jefferson played the violin. Maybe it soothed the animals.

The Great Inventor

Jefferson liked to invent things. He invented a cipher wheel to write secret codes. He also invented a revolving book holder. It held five books. Jefferson loved to read!

Jefferson by the Numbers

1 Number of universities Jefferson founded: the University of Virginia.

24 Number of counties named after him.

33 Jefferson's age when he wrote the Declaration of Independence.

1,230 Number of pounds a cheese that was given to him in 1802, weighed.

6,487 Number of books he sold to help start the Library of Congress.

Jefferson Memorial

FAST FACT

Every day, Jefferson bathed his feet in freezing water. He thought it would prevent colds.

Campaign Corner

In 1800, Jefferson was vice president. John Adams was president. They ran against each other. Jefferson won.

James MADISON

MEET MADISON

#4

Term: 1809–1817
First Lady:
Dolley Madison

Madison's Look

- Madison was the smallest president.
- He was five feet, four inches tall and weighed only about one hundred pounds.
- He was the first president to wear long pants instead of short breeches. Long pants, short man.

Family Man

- Madison had no children, but he is called the Father of the Constitution and the Father of the Bill of Rights.
- He is also a Founding Father. So when you enjoy free speech, thank Father Madison!

True or False

1. Madison wrote much of the Constitution.
2. Madison wrote the Declaration of Independence.
3. When the White House was burned in the War of 1812, Dolley saved a portrait of George Washington.
4. Both of his vice presidents died while in office.
5. Madison said on his deathbed, "I always talk better lying down."

Answers: 1.T, 2.F, 3.T, 4.T, 5.T

FAST FACT

James and Dolley were the first to serve ice cream in the White House. A sundae on Sunday.

Campaign Corner

Madison's opponents made fun of his size. Still, Madison won by a landslide. He also won a second term even though we went to war in 1812. Good thing the United States won the war!

MEET MONROE

Term: 1817–1825
First Lady:
  Elizabeth Monroe

Yes Sir, Colonel!

- Monroe was the last president to have served as an enlisted officer in the Revolutionary War.
- He was shot in the Battle of Trenton. The bullet stayed in his arm for the rest of his life.
- Monroe was proud of his army service. He liked to be called Colonel.

Road Trip

Monroe was the first president to tour the country. He spent about fifteen weeks on the road. Luckily, our country was not that big then!

Family Man

- Monroe traveled a lot with his family.
- In Paris, he and his wife saved Madame Lafayette from the guillotine during the French Revolution.
- Monroe believed that both girls and boys should be educated, so his daughters were well taught.

In the famous painting of George Washington crossing the Delaware, Monroe is holding the flag.

FAST FACT

The first U.S. public high school opened in 1821.

Campaign Corner

Monroe ran unopposed in 1820. The time was called the Era of Good Feelings.

Term: 1825–1829
First Lady:
  Louisa Adams

Adams's Look

- Adams did not like to dress up.
- Maybe that's why he skinny-dipped in the Potomac River behind the White House. He piled all his clothes nearby.
- He also wore the same hat every day for ten years.

Family Man

- John Quincy Adams was the son of President John Adams.
- He called himself JQA so as not to be confused with his father.
- His wife was the only English-born First Lady.
- He named his son George Washington after his favorite leader.

The Writer

- Adams kept a diary from the time he was eleven years old. He tried to write in his diary every day until he died. Today, the Massachusetts Historical Society posts his diary entries on Twitter.
- He also published a book of poetry.

FAST FACT

He was the first president to have a pool table in the White House.

Campaign Corner

Adams lost his bid for reelection to Andrew Jackson, but he later won election to Congress. He was the only president to become a congressman after serving as president.

Andrew JACKSON

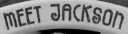
MEET JACKSON

Term: 1829–1837
First Lady:
Rachel Jackson
(She died before he became president.)

The Fighting Man

- Jackson joined the army at thirteen as a volunteer.
- He was a prisoner of war during the American Revolution.
- In the War of 1812, he won the battle of New Orleans, beating the British, even though the war had officially ended.
- He also fought in the First Seminole War. The Creek Indians called him Sharp Knife.

Home, Sweet Home

Jackson was the first president born in a log cabin. The cabin had no plumbing. Maybe that's why he had running water and bathrooms installed in the White House.

Hey, I'm First

- Jackson was the first congressman from the new state of Tennessee, in 1796.
- He fought many duels before he became president. In one duel, a bullet lodged next to his heart. The doctors couldn't remove it, but he survived.
- Jackson was the first president to ride a train.

1st

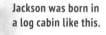

Jackson was born in a log cabin like this.

FAST FACT

Those who opposed Jackson called him King Andrew. Those who admired him called his time the Era of the Common Man. He preferred the nickname Old Hickory.

Campaign Corner

Jackson had a group of friends as advisers. They met in the White House kitchen to discuss policies. Some called them the Kitchen Cabinet.

Martin VAN BUREN

Term: 1837–1841
First Lady:
Hannah Van Buren
(She died before he
became president.)

#8

Van Buren's Look

- Van Buren liked to wear fine clothes.
- He had large muttonchop sideburns.
- He liked fine things, too. At the White House, he used finger bowls. People rinsed their fingers during a meal. Now that's clean.

Nicknames

Van Buren's nickname was Old Kinderhook because he was from Kinderhook, New York. Clubs formed to support him in politics. They were called the OK clubs. Their slogan was "OK," which is how the phrase "OK" was born. OK?

Born in the U.S.A.

Van Buren was the first president to be born a U.S. citizen. Previous presidents were born British citizens, because America was a colony at the time. English was his second language. His first language was Dutch.

This statue of Van Buren is in Kinderhook.

FAST FACT

Van Buren kept two tiger cubs as pets.

Campaign Corner
Van Buren was the only president to run for reelection without a vice president. He lost.

William Henry HARRISON

MEET HARRISON

Term: 1841
First Lady:
  Anna Harrison

Harrison's Campaign

- Harrison came from a rich Virginia family.
- However, he campaigned as "one of us." His campaign image was that he was born in a log cabin (he wasn't).
- He was poor (he wasn't).
- He had worked hard to get where he was (he did). You can't always judge a president by his "cover."

Long Speech, Short Presidency

Harrison gave the longest inaugural speech in history. It was almost two hours! The day was cold and rainy. He caught a cold and died. His presidency was the shortest term.

Family Man

- Harrison's grandson Benjamin Harrison became the twenty-third president.
- Harrison's father signed the Declaration of Independence.

Harrison lived in this mansion.

FAST FACT

Harrison studied to be a doctor.

Campaign Corner

Harrison was the first president to have an organized political campaign. He campaigned as a war hero. He won a battle at Tippecanoe. His slogan was "Tippecanoe and Tyler, too."

Term: 1841–1845
First Ladies:
Letitia Tyler (She died during his presidency);
Julia Tyler

#10

His Accidency

- Tyler was serving as vice president when President Harrison died.
- Some say that Tyler was playing marbles at his home in Virginia when he was told he had become president.
- Those who opposed him called him His Accidency. He hated the nickname.
- He refused to open or read any mail addressed to "the Acting President." "Mr. President," please!

Family Man

- Tyler had fifteen children. He was the president with the most children.
- His youngest child, Pearl, died in 1947. That's more than one hundred years after her father became president.

Peace, Please

After he retired from the presidency, the Civil War started. Tyler had tried to negotiate peace between the North and the South, but Congress rejected all of his ideas. Finally, Tyler voted for Virginia to leave the nation and join the Confederacy. He was elected to the Confederate Congress.

FAST FACT

Tyler and his wife played the violin and guitar at parties. Rock on!

Campaign Corner

Tyler was the first vice president to become president upon the death of the previous president. Some people did not believe he should have the full power of the presidency.

Term: 1845–1849
First Lady:
Sarah Polk

Nicknames

- Polk was a popular president. Many called him the People's Choice.
- He was from Tennessee, like President Jackson, so others called him Young Hickory. Luckily, he liked Jackson, so he took it as a compliment.
- People could have called him Moneybags, too. Polk didn't trust banks. He hid his money in bags around his home.

Fun . . . NOT

The White House was quiet when Polk was president. His wife, Sarah, did not believe in dancing, music, or playing cards. There were no parties at the White House.

Work, Work, and Work Some More

Polk had trouble trusting people to do things. So he did almost all of his work himself. He worked around the clock. Maybe it's because of his childhood, when he worked on his father's farm from sunrise to sunset. He learned to work early, and long!

This is what the White House looked like when Polk was president.

FAST FACT

Say Cheese!

Polk was the first president to have his photo taken.

Campaign Corner

When Polk ran for office, he promised not to run for a second term if he won. He kept his promise.

Term: 1849–1850
First Lady:
Margaret Taylor

#12

Family Man

- Taylor came from a famous family.
- His relatives had come over on the Mayflower.
- President Madison was his cousin.
- Because his family moved to the frontier, Taylor had no formal education. He was a terrible speller. Still, he did well for himself!

Ride on . . . Sidesaddle?

Taylor was an army general and a war hero. However, he did one odd thing. He rode his horse sidesaddle. Both his legs dangled on the same side. He rode this way in battle. Tallyho!

Bad Fourth of July

In 1850, Taylor celebrated the Fourth of July. At the ceremony at the Washington Memorial, he ate many different foods. He ate cherries, pickles, and milk. It was a hot day. Taylor got sick and died five days later.

Taylor rode sidesaddle.

FAST FACT

Taylor did not vote until he was sixty-two.

Campaign Corner
Taylor campaigned under the slogan "Old Rough and Ready." The slogan played up that he'd been in the army for almost forty years.

Term: 1850–1853
First Lady:
   Abigail Fillmore

#13

Log Cabin to White House

- Fillmore was a self-made man. He worked hard.
- He went to a one-room school.
- He was elected to Congress.
- Then he was vice president.
- Finally, he made it to the White House. It was a long, tough road!

Let's Trade

Fillmore sent Admiral Matthew Perry to Japan in 1853. He wanted to trade with Japan. He also sent warships. Japan began to trade with the United States.

交
易

(Japanese for "trade")

Family Man

- Millard's wife, Abigail, encouraged his love of reading.
- They later established the first permanent library for first families at the White House. They had more than four thousand books in their private collection. They loved books!

FAST FACT

Fillmore had the first stove to cook on in the White House. But no one, not even the cook, knew exactly how to use it! Salad, anyone?

Campaign Corner

Fillmore had no vice president while he was president. It's a good thing nothing happened to him while he was in office.

Term: 1853–1857
First Lady:
Jane Pierce

#14

Pierce's Look

- Franklin Pierce was called Handsome Frank. People described him as charming, dashing, and good-looking.
- He was also called Young Hickory of the Granite Hills because he was from New Hampshire, and was a supporter of Andrew Jackson.

We Like Pierce

Pierce was the only president to keep his cabinet for his whole term. No one quit. No one was fired. That was an amazing feat.

Write About Me

- Pierce went to Bowdoin College, in Maine. One classmate was the writer Nathaniel Hawthorne.
- When Pierce ran for president, Hawthorne wrote a biography of him. He wrote good things about his friend. Do you think it helped him win?

Nathaniel Hawthorne

Pierce's Cabinet

FAST FACT

Pierce had the first Christmas tree in the White House.

Campaign Corner

Pierce fought in the Mexican War. On the field, he fell off his horse. His opponent's campaign accused him of being a coward.

James BUCHANAN

MEET BUCHANAN

Term: 1857–1861
First Lady:
  none

Buchanan's Look

- Buchanan was six feet tall.
- He was heavyset.
- His vision was not good. In one eye, he was nearsighted. In the other eye, he was farsighted. So he often tilted his head to the side.

Family Man

- Buchanan was the only president who never married. His niece, Harriet Lane, served as hostess at the White House.
- Some say people thought Buchanan was lonely, so they sent him pets. He had a herd of elephants, two bald eagles, and a large Newfoundland dog.

Eat Up!

- Buchanan loved both French and German food.
- He loved big, fancy meals. He served lobster and wild turkey.
- At his inaugural ball, he served twelve hundred quarts of ice cream!

TELEGRAM

DEAR VICKI,
HOW ARE YOU?
JIMMY

FAST FACT

Buchanan was the first president to send a transatlantic telegram. He sent it to England's Queen Victoria.

Campaign Corner

Buchanan first ran for president in 1844. He tried again in 1848 and 1852. Finally, he won in 1856. He was determined!

Term: 1861–1865
First Lady:
Mary Todd Lincoln

Family Man

- Lincoln was the tallest president. He was six feet, four inches.
- He was the first president to wear a beard.
- People described him as thin and gangly. "Gangly" means long limbed.
- He often wore a stovepipe hat, in which he sometimes kept important papers.

Speech, Speech, Speech

Lincoln was famous for his speeches. He loved words and wrote all his own speeches. One of his most famous is the Gettysburg Address.

Sad Day

- Lincoln attended a play at Washington, D.C.'s Ford's Theatre in 1865. There, an actor, John Wilkes Booth, shot him. He died about nine hours later.
- Lincoln was the first president to be assassinated.
- Today, we honor Lincoln in many ways. He appears on coins, stamps, and in memorials.

Lincoln Memorial

FAST FACT

Lincoln made Thanksgiving a national holiday.

Campaign Corner

Lincoln campaigned as "Honest Abe," and posters showed him splitting rails. The image helped him win.

Term: 1865–1869
First Lady:
  Eliza Johnson

The Apprentice

At fourteen, Johnson became a tailor's apprentice. After about two years, he ran away. Still, Johnson continued to make his own clothes.

Johnson campaign button

A Big Deal

The United States bought Alaska when Johnson was president. The price was $7,200,000. Many people thought it was a bad deal. Then gold and oil were discovered. We paid about 2¢ an acre. Do you think it was a good deal?

Johnson by the Numbers

0 Number of years Johnson went to school. His wife taught him to read, write, and do math.

1 Number of votes that saved him from impeachment.

10 Number of years that Johnson served as a congressman.

21 Johnson's age when elected mayor of Greenville, TN.

1865 The year Johnson became president.

Alaska

FAST FACT

Johnson loved mice. He would not kill them. He left water and flour for them instead.

Campaign Corner

President Lincoln was a Republican, and Johnson was Democrat. Johnson agreed to run with Lincoln as his vice president. He did not join the Republican Party.

MEET GRANT

Term: 1869–1877
First Lady:
   Julia Grant

The General

Grant led the Union army to victory during the Civil War. During the war, Grant thought it was bad luck to retrace his steps. So he never did. He won battles by going forward.

Family Man

- Grant and his wife decided to visit their children instead of joining the Lincolns at Ford's Theatre the night President Lincoln was killed.

- When Grant left the presidency, he was broke. So he wrote his autobiography. He finished it days before he died. It became a bestseller and earned around $500,000! A nice gift for his family.

A Big Tomb

Grant and his wife are buried in Grant's tomb in New York City. It is the largest tomb of its kind in North America.

Grant campaign poster

FAST FACT

Grant once received a speeding ticket when riding a horse.

Campaign Corner

Grant was the first president to have a woman run against him. Virginia Woodhull ran as a candidate for the Equal Rights Party.

Rutherford B. HAYES

Term: 1877–1881
First Lady:
    Lucy Hayes

#19

Family Man

- Rutherford Hayes was the first president to graduate from law school. He went to Harvard.
- Lucy was the first president's wife to graduate from college.
- She was also the first wife officially to be called First Lady. They were the first to have an Easter egg roll at the White House. It is still a tradition today.

Hayes's Look

Hayes was noted for his beard. In fact, his beard was so long, it dipped into his soup. Pass the napkin, please.

Nicknames

- Some people called Hayes His Fraudulency. When some electoral votes were questioned, a special commission finally declared him the winner. He took the oath in secret.
- Lucy was called Lemonade Lucy. She served lemonade instead of alcohol in the White House.

White House
Easter egg roll

FAST FACT

Hayes was the first president to visit the West Coast.

Campaign Corner

Hayes was the first president elected who lost the popular vote. He pledged not to run again if he won. He didn't.

James A. GARFIELD

MEET GARFIELD

Term: 1881
First Lady:
  Lucretia Garfield

Political Man

Garfield was a congressman when he ran for the senate in 1880. He won. Then he won the nomination for president. He won the presidency, too. So for a short period, he was a U.S. congressman, a senator-elect, and a president-elect. Busy man!

Man Overboard

At sixteen, Garfield wanted to go to sea, so he worked on a boat on the Erie Canal. It was an odd job for him. Garfield couldn't swim, and he fell overboard around fourteen times. Man overboard, again!

Garfield by the Numbers

2 Garfield's age when his father died. He and his mother were close. She lived with him at the White House. She was the first mother of a president to be present when he was sworn in.

7 The seventh and last president to be born in a log cabin.

23 Garfield's age when he entered college. He started late, but became president of a college by age twenty-five.

49 Garfield's age when he became U.S. president and the age he died. He was assassinated.

$50,000 The salary he earned as president.

FAST FACT

Garfield was the first left-handed president, but he could write with both hands. To make people laugh, he wrote Latin with one hand and Greek with the other hand.

Campaign Corner

Garfield was the first president to campaign in English and Spanish. He also ran a "front porch" campaign. He gave speeches when people visited him on his porch.

MEET ARTHUR

#21

Term: 1881–1885
First Lady:
 Ellen Arthur
 (She died before he
 became President.)

Lawn Sale

Arthur didn't move into the White House right away. He wanted it redone. So he had about twenty-four wagons full of unwanted furniture sold on the White House lawn. He sold it all for around $8,000. Today, it would be priceless!

Arthur's Look

- Arthur liked to wear nice clothes.
- He was called Elegant Arthur and also Gentleman Boss.
  - Arthur is said to have owned more than eighty pairs of pants. They came in handy because he changed his pants several times a day.

Freedom Fighter

Arthur was a lawyer. In New York, he defended an African American woman who was denied a seat in a streetcar because of her race. He won the case. He fought for civil rights. Good job!

FAST FACT

Arthur took the oath of the president twice. Once in his home in New York, and again in Washington, D.C.

Campaign Corner

Arthur was the first president to have his citizenship challenged. Many people believed he was born in Canada. He was born in Vermont.

First Term: 1885–1889
First Lady:
Frances Cleveland

#22

Family Man

- Grover Cleveland was the only president to get married in the White House.
- His wife, Frances, was the youngest First Lady. She was twenty-one.

Nicknames

- Cleveland's real first name was Stephen, but he preferred being called Grover, his middle name.
- Cleveland was a big man who weighed more than 250 pounds. He was called Uncle Jumbo.
- His daughter Ruth was called Baby Ruth by the newspapers. The candy bar Baby Ruth is named after her.

Cleveland by the Numbers

2 Number of speeches Cleveland gave during his first presidential campaign.

6 Cleveland was a sixth cousin of President Grant.

8 Number of brothers and sisters he had.

38 Number of U.S. states when he was president.

$1,000 Cleveland's face was once on the $1,000 bill. That denomination is not in circulation today.

FAST FACT

Cleveland was once a sheriff in upstate New York. He was also the local hangman.

SHERIFF

Campaign Corner

Cleveland won the popular vote in presidential elections in 1884, 1888, and 1892. He won the presidency in 1884 and 1892.

MEET HARRISON

Term: 1889–1893
First Lady:
Caroline Harrison

#23

The Flag

Harrison loved to see the flag flying. He had the U.S. flag flown above the White House and other government buildings. Schools started flying the flag, too.

Speech, Speech, Speech

- Harrison loved to give speeches. In a period of about thirty days, he gave 140 different speeches. That's more than four per day.

- Harrison recorded a thirty-six-second talk, too. That makes him the first president to record a speech. He loved to talk!

Lights, Lights, and More Lights

Harrison was the first president to use electric lights in the White House. However, he and his wife were afraid to turn them off. They thought they'd get shocked. They must have paid a big electric bill!

FAST FACT

Harrison was formal and quiet. His opponents called him the Human Iceberg. That's cold.

Campaign Corner

Harrison lost the popular vote by more than ninety thousand votes. However, he won the electoral college votes, 233 to 168, which gave him the presidency.

Second Term: 1893–1897
First Lady:
Frances Cleveland

Nicknames

Cleveland liked to use his veto power. He vetoed more bills than the previous twenty-two presidents together. He vetoed more than four hundred bills. He earned the nickname Old Veto.

Family Man

- Grover and his wife had three daughters and two sons.
- He was the only president to have a child born in the White House: his daughter Esther.

Secret Operation

In 1893, the country was in a financial crisis. Cleveland needed an operation. He had mouth cancer. He didn't want the public to panic. So he had the operation on a boat on the Long Island Sound. The operation was a success. It was kept secret for about twenty years.

FAST FACT

Cleveland loved fishing and published a book on fishing.

Campaign Corner

Cleveland was the only president to serve nonconsecutive terms. He was the twenty-second and twenty-fourth president.

William McKINLEY

MEET McKINLEY

Term: 1897–1901
First Lady:
Ida McKinley

McKinley campaign poster of eagle, flag, McKinley, and Roosevelt

McKinley's Look

- McKinley liked a clean look.
- He was the first president without a mustache or a beard for a period of more than twenty-five years.
- He wore a red carnation in his lapel every day for good luck.

No Yellow

McKinley's wife, Ida, hated the color yellow. No rooms in the White House could be painted yellow. Even the yellow flowers in the gardens were ripped out. Yellow was not mellow for her.

Fate?

McKinley was at an exhibit in Buffalo, New York, shaking hands. He could shake thirty hands a minute. He gave his lucky red carnation to a little girl in line. A short time after, he was shot. He was rushed to a hospital in an ambulance, but he died eight days later.

Yankee Doodle Dandy

FAST FACT

McKinley had a pet parrot that could whistle "Yankee Doodle Dandy."

Campaign Corner

McKinley was the first president to use a telephone to campaign for office. His inauguration was also the first to be filmed.

Term: 1901–1909
First Lady:
Edith Roosevelt

#26

The Teddy Bear

Roosevelt was a big hunter, but he also had a big heart. He refused to shoot a bear when hunting. Soon people began selling toy bears called Teddy bears, short for Theodore. Roosevelt was the "father" of the teddy bear.

Father of National Parks

Roosevelt loved the outdoors. He set aside almost two hundred million acres for parks, reserves, and wildlife refuges. Take a walk in a national park and thank Roosevelt.

Roosevelt's Firsts

- Roosevelt was a man of many firsts. He was the first president to travel outside the United States when he went to Panama.
- He was the first to ride in a car, fly in an airplane, and descend in a submarine.
- He was the first American to win the Nobel Peace Prize.

FAST FACT

Roosevelt liked to walk on stilts. He and his family members all owned stilts.

Campaign Corner

Roosevelt campaigned as big-business buster. One slogan he used was "Speak softly, and carry a big stick." He campaigned from his front porch.

William Howard TAFT

Term: 1909–1913
First Lady:
Helen Taft

Big Sports Fan

- Taft loved sports.
- He played tennis and loved to dance.
- He was the first president to play golf.
- He also was the first president to throw the opening ball for baseball season. Play ball!

This Tub's for You

- Taft was called Big Bill.
- He was six feet, two inches tall, and weighed more than 330 pounds. He was our largest president.
- Taft once got stuck in the White House tub. Six attendants had to pull him out. So he had a new tub put in, big enough to hold four men.

Taft's Best Job

After serving as president, Taft was appointed the chief justice of the Supreme Court. He liked that job better than being president.

Taft as Supreme
Court Justice

FAST FACT

Taft was the first president to own a car. He had the White House stables converted into a garage.

Campaign Corner

Former president Roosevelt supported Taft when he ran for president in 1908. When Taft ran for a second term, Roosevelt ran against him as a third-party candidate. Taft lost.

Woodrow WILSON

MEET WILSON

#28

Term: 1913–1921
First Ladies:
Ellen Wilson (She died during his presidency);
Edith Wilson

The Professor

- Wilson didn't learn to read until he was almost twelve.
- He is the only president to have earned a doctorate.
- He was president of Princeton University.
- His nickname was the Professor. Smart man!

Peace

Wilson wanted World War I to be the last war. He started the League of Nations, whose purpose was for countries to work together. The League of Nations failed. Today, we have the United Nations. It has the same goals. Wilson won the Nobel Peace Prize for his efforts.

Wilson by the Numbers

28 He was born on December 28, 1856.

28 He was our twenty-eighth president.

56 28 + 28 = 56. Fifty-six is the year he was born and the age he was when he became president.

The United Nations

FAST FACT

Wilson let sheep graze on the White House lawn to raise wool for the war effort.

Campaign Corner

Wilson held the first press conference. He held them regularly. His conferences won him votes.

Warren G. HARDING

MEET HARDING

Term: 1921–1923
First Lady:
   Florence Harding

Harding's Firsts

- Harding was the first president to travel to his inauguration in a car.
- He was the first to own a radio.
- He was the first to have a golf course named after him.

Your Deal

Harding liked to play poker. He played at least twice a week with his cabinet members. Once he gambled and lost a complete set of White House china.

Solve It!

Harding died in office. He was on a tour out west. No one is sure what he died of. Some say a heart attack. Some say a stroke. Some say poison.

FAST FACT

Harding was the first president to visit Alaska territory.

Campaign Corner

Harding was the first president to hire a speechwriter. He was also the first president to give a speech on the radio.

Term: 1923–1929
First Lady:
Grace Coolidge

Party Central

- The Coolidges had lots of parties at the White House.
- Coolidge was silent, but his wife was not. She knew sign language and was good friends with Helen Keller.
- Coolidge loved to take naps and supposedly slept more than any other president.

ZZZ

The Joker

Coolidge was a man of few words. Nicknamed Silent Cal, he once played a "silent" joke. A woman said she had a bet that she could get him to say more than two words. He said, "You lose!"

Ride 'Em, Cowboy

Coolidge had an electric horse installed in the White House. He rode it almost every day. Giddyup!

FAST FACT

Coolidge was the first president to have his inauguration broadcast on the radio.

Campaign Corner

Coolidge's slogan was "Keep cool with Coolidge." He beat out Henry Ford for his party's nomination.

Herbert HOOVER

MEET HOOVER

Term: 1929–1933
First Lady:
Lou Hoover

#31

Go, Hoover!

Hoover exercised every morning, rain or shine. He often threw a medicine ball around for thirty minutes. Catch!

Family Man

- The Hoovers both graduated from Stanford University.
- Their two sons graduated from Stanford, too.
- Herbert and his wife spoke Chinese. When they didn't want people to know what they were saying, they spoke in Chinese.

(Chinese for "welcome")

Hoover by the Numbers

1 First president to have an asteroid named after him.

40 The age he became a millionaire. He donated his president's salary to charity.

53 Number of schools in the United States named after him.

89 Number of honorary degrees he received.

1929 Year the stock market crashed.

FAST FACT

Hoover was the first president to have a phone on his desk.

Campaign Corner

His slogan was "A chicken in every pot and a car in every garage." The Great Depression ruined his slogan.

Franklin Delano ROOSEVELT

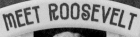

MEET ROOSEVELT

Term: 1933–1945
First Lady:
  Eleanor Roosevelt

#32

I Didn't Know That

Roosevelt had polio and used a wheelchair. Most Americans at the time were unaware of his disability. Photographers did not take his picture when he was in his wheelchair.

Hobbies

- Roosevelt liked to build model ships.
- He also collected more than a million postage stamps. His stamp collection sold for more than $200,000. That's a lot of postage!

All in the Family

- President Theodore Roosevelt was Franklin's fifth cousin. He gave Eleanor away at their wedding.
- Eleanor often gave speeches for Franklin.
- The family served hot dogs to the king and queen of England. They liked American food.

FAST FACT

Roosevelt was the first president to deliver a speech on television.

Campaign Corner

Roosevelt used the radio effectively in his campaign. As president, he gave "fireside chats." The chats worked. He was elected president a record four times.

35

MEET TRUMAN

Term: 1945–1953
First Lady:
Bess Truman

#33

Family Man

- Harry and Bess are the only president and first lady to graduate from the same high school.
- Their daughter, Margaret, sang in public. One critic did not like her singing. People said Harry stated that if he saw the critic, he'd punch him in the nose!

Hobbies

- Truman loved to play the piano. As a child, he would wake up at 5 a.m. and practice for two hours.
- He also loved to read. He said that by the time he was fifteen, he had read every book in his town's public library.
- He must have liked to draw, too. He helped design the presidential seal.

The Letter "S"

The letter "S" in Truman's name does not stand for anything. It's just the letter "S." Editors argue if there should be a period after it or not. Truman said no, but this may have been a joke. What do you think?

S.

FAST FACT

Truman was the first president to travel underwater in a modern submarine.

Campaign Corner

Truman conducted a "whistle-stop" campaign. He rode a train. The train stopped, the whistle blew, and Truman gave a speech. His family lived on the train while he campaigned.

Dwight D. EISENHOWER

MEET EISENHOWER

Term: 1953–1961
First Lady:
Mamie Eisenhower

#34

Family Man

- Eisenhower and his family spent time at Camp David, a retreat for the president and his family. The place was special to Ike. He named it after his grandson, David.

- David Eisenhower grew up to have a family connection with another president. He married President Nixon's daughter Julie.

Camp David

Sports

- Eisenhower was the first president to have a pilot's license.

- He also once played minor league baseball.

- His favorite game was golf. Eisenhower had a putting green installed at the White House. Because he played about one hundred rounds of golf a year, it came in handy.

Army vs. Navy

Eisenhower was too old to enter the naval academy when he wanted to attend, so he went to West Point and into the army. He became a five-star general and commanded all U.S. troops in Europe during World War II.

FAST FACT

Eisenhower was the first president to appear on color television.

Campaign Corner

Eisenhower was the first presidential candidate to run a TV commercial. His slogan was "I like Ike." Many people liked Ike. He won by a landslide.

MEET KENNEDY

Term: 1961–1963
First Lady:
  Jacqueline Kennedy

#35

Lincoln vs. Kennedy

Presidents Lincoln and Kennedy share some odd facts. Lincoln became president in 1860, Kennedy in 1960. Lincoln's secretary's last name was Kennedy. Kennedy's secretary's last name was Lincoln. Both presidents were assassinated. Their vice presidents became presidents, and both vice presidents had the last name Johnson. Eerie!

Kennedy by the Numbers

1 Kennedy won the Pulitzer Prize for his book *Profiles in Courage.* He is the only president to win this award.

8 Number of his brothers and sisters.

43 Age he was elected president. He is the youngest elected president.

1,037 Numbers of days Kennedy served as president before he was killed.

$1,000,000 Amount of money he received from his father when he turned twenty-one.

Kennedy's Look

- Kennedy was called handsome and charming.
- He wore corrective shoes because one leg was shorter than the other.
- Some say he hired a drama coach to help him with public speaking. Listen to one of his speeches, what do you think?

FAST FACT

Kennedy was the first Boy Scout to become president.

Campaign Corner

Kennedy debated his opponent, Richard Nixon, on television. Kennedy looked good on TV, but Nixon did not. Some say the debate helped Kennedy win the election.

Term: 1963–1969
First Lady:
  Claudia "Lady Bird" Johnson

Gifts from Johnson

Johnson gave away electric toothbrushes as gifts.

Family Man

- Johnson came from a family of Texas ranchers and farmers.
- He liked to wear a Stetson cowboy hat.
- His family had a tradition: Everyone had the same initials: LBJ. He was Lyndon Baines Johnson. He called his wife Lady Bird, and his daughters were named Lynda Bird and Luci Baines.

Phones and TVs

- Johnson had three TVs in his bedroom so he could watch the three network news shows at the same time.
- He had phones everywhere. He had them in his cars, boats, planes, and even the swimming pool, on a floating raft.

Johnson being sworn in as president

FAST FACT

Johnson was the first president sworn in by a woman, Sarah Hughes, after President Kennedy was assassinated.

Campaign Corner

Lyndon Johnson used the slogan "All the way with LBJ." The voters went with him. He won by a landslide.

Richard M. NIXON

MEET NIXON

Term: 1969–1974
First Lady:
Pat Nixon

#37

Sad Chapter in History

Nixon had to resign as president because of a scandal named Watergate. He is the only president to resign.

Family Man

- Richard's middle name, Milhous, was his mother's maiden name.
- She named most of her sons after English kings. Richard was named after Richard the Lion-Hearted.
- His daughter Julie married President Eisenhower's grandson, David.
- Nixon's daughter Tricia was married in the White House Rose Garden.

Hello

Nixon made a lot of phone calls. He called Neil Armstrong on the moon. He also called his friends and staff late at night when he couldn't sleep. One night, he made about fifty calls.

NIXON'S THE ONE!

FAST FACT

Nixon was the first president to visit mainland China.

Campaign Corner

In the 1972 election, Nixon won forty-nine out of fifty states. He spent about $60 million on his campaign, a lot of money at the time.

Family Man

- Gerald and his wife, Betty, had creative jobs.
- He worked as a model while he was in law school.
- Betty was a dancer. Gerald loved to dance, too. He would dance until one in the morning at state dinners.
- Their daughter, Susan, held her prom in the White House.

Sports

Ford is considered the most athletic president. The National Football League recruited him. He played golf, jogged, sailed, skied, and swam. He played sports with his right hand, and with his left hand, ate and, when sitting, wrote.

Mr. Nice Guy President

- Ford is the first and only president who was not an elected vice president or president.
- He was appointed vice president when President Nixon's vice president resigned. When Nixon resigned, Ford became president.
- He earned the nickname Mr. Nice Guy. The people trusted him.

EXPERIENCE COUNTS
Elect Gerald R. FORD in '76

Ford playing football

FAST FACT

Ford was the only president who was an Eagle Scout.

Gerald Ford's Eagle Scout badge.

Campaign Corner

His campaign slogan was "He's making us proud again." It is said he was the first president to hire someone just to write jokes.

MEET CARTER

Term: 1977–1981
First Lady:
   Rosalyn Carter

Carter's Look

- Carter hated to dress up.
- He never wore a hat.
- He told people to call him Jimmy, not James. When he was sworn in as president, he used that nickname.
- He acted informal, too. He told the Secret Service to stop opening doors for him.

Anchors Aweigh

Carter is the only president to have graduated from the U.S. Naval Academy. He served on ships in both the Atlantic and Pacific Oceans. He helped develop nuclear submarines for the Navy.

Family Man

- Carter's family were peanut farmers.
- He liked playing outdoors. At the White House, he and his family threw Frisbees on the lawn.
- Carter and his family took a speed-reading course. He could read 2,000 words per minute. Now that's a fast read!

nuclear submarine

FAST FACT

He was the first president born in a hospital and not at home.

Campaign Corner

His campaign slogan was "A leader, for a change." He campaigned as a Washington outsider. It was a close race.

Ronald REAGAN

MEET REAGAN

Term: 1981–1989
First Lady: Nancy Reagan

#40

Senior Statesman

Reagan was the oldest president. He was sixty-nine when he was elected.

Jelly Beans

- Reagan was famous for loving jelly beans.
- For his inauguration, blueberry jelly beans were made. More than three tons of jelly beans were shipped to the White House.
- Guests were served red, white, and blue jelly beans. What's your favorite jelly bean flavor?

Jobs

- Reagan was a lifeguard for six summers. He rescued seventy-seven people in all.
- He also worked as a radio baseball announcer.
- Reagan was the first president who was a movie actor. He knew how to work a camera. Some called him the Great Communicator.

RONALD REAGAN

FAST FACT

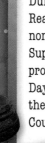

Reagan was the oldest president in history, at age sixty-nine.

Campaign Corner

During his campaign, Reagan promised to nominate a woman to the Supreme Court. He kept his promise. In 1981, Sandra Day O'Connor became the first woman Supreme Court justice.

43

Term: 1989–1993
First Lady:
   Barbara Bush

Family Man

- There are three generations of the Bush family in politics. George's father was a senator from Connecticut. His son George Walker became president. Another son, Jeb, was governor of Florida.
- Even his dogs were famous. They "wrote" the bestsellers *Millie's Book* and *C. Fred's Story*.

Food Star

He was the first president to admit he hated broccoli. He had it banned from the White House. What food would you ban from your house?

Sports

- Bush played first base in college. His team reached the finals of the College World Series twice.
- Bush's other favorite sports were tennis, boating, and fishing.

Bush played baseball in college.

FAST FACT

During World War II, Bush, at age nineteen, became one of the youngest pilots in the U.S. Navy.

Campaign Corner

During his campaign, Bush said, "Read my lips: no new taxes." He won, but had to raise taxes.

44

William J. CLINTON

Term: 1993–2001
First Lady:
  Hillary Rodham
  Clinton

#42

American Idol

- Clinton collected books about the lives of the presidents.
- When he was sixteen, Clinton met President Kennedy. After the meeting, Clinton decided to go into politics.
- He was the youngest governor in the United States at age thirty-two.

All in the Family

- Bill's wife, Hillary Rodham Clinton, is in politics, too.
- She was the first former First Lady to be later elected a U.S. senator.
- She then became secretary of state.

Music Man

Clinton won several music scholarships. He turned them down. He played the saxophone in high school. Today, he still plays the sax.

Clinton giving a speech

FAST FACT

He worked as a Red Cross volunteer.

Campaign Corner

Clinton's campaign slogan was "Putting people first."

45

George W. BUSH

MEET BUSH

Term: 2001–2009
First Lady:
  Laura Bush

#43

Family Man

- Bush was the second president to be the son of a president.
- He was the first president to have twins.
- His nickname, Dubya, is how some Texans pronounce the letter "W," his middle initial.

"W"

¡Hola!

Bush was the first president to give the same radio speech from the Oval Office in English and Spanish. Bush was also the first president to give a video tour of the White House online.

Hola! Hello!

Sports

- Bush wanted to be Willie Mays when he grew up. He loved baseball.
- He was the only president to have played Little League baseball as a boy.
- He had a T-ball field installed at the White House.

FAST FACT

Bush banned jeans in the Oval Office, but he wore his cowboy boots to meetings.

Campaign Corner

The Supreme Court decided the 2000 presidential election. Al Gore had won the popular vote, but after a contested election result in Florida, the court voted, 5–4, in favor of Bush.

Barack OBAMA

Term: 2009–
First Lady:
Michelle Obama

#44

Book-Loving Author

- Obama has written two bestselling books.
- He won two Grammy Awards for audio recordings of *Dreams from My Father* and *The Audacity of Hope*.
- He has also read all the Harry Potter books.

Sports

- Obama loves sports. During his campaign, he sometimes watched sports instead of the news on TV.
- He played basketball in high school. He still plays basketball at the White House.
- He also likes boxing. He owns a pair of boxing gloves autographed by former world champ Muhammad Ali.

Obama by the Numbers

2 Number of daughters.

6 He is the sixth left-handed president of the last twelve presidents.

11 Size of his shoes. He owns four identical pairs.

200 Number of pounds he can bench press.

1,000 Number of YouTube videos he had in 2008.

FAST FACT

He hates ice cream. He worked in an ice-cream shop as a teenager.

Campaign Corner

Obama is the first African American president. His slogan was "Change we can believe in."

CONGRATULATIONS, MR. PRESIDENT

Barack Obama

For the 2012 presidential election, use the stickers in this book to create this winner's page. Place the election winner in the winner's circle. Then decorate the page.

Democrat

Symbol of Winning Party

Presidential Seal

The White House

HOW WELL DO YOU KNOW OUR U.S. PRESIDENTS?

In this fact-filled book, you'll discover which president was the first to:

★ ride in a submarine

★ campaign from his front porch

★ have an asteroid named after him

★ be born in a hospital

★ make a phone call to the moon

And much more! You can also use the sticker sheet to design your own page about the winner of this year's history-making election.

■ SCHOLASTIC

www.scholastic.com

This edition is available for distribution only through the school market.

Reading Level: 2.5
Guided Reading Level: T
Lexile®: IG570L

ISBN 978-0-545-

9 780545 505

P8-CAZ-288

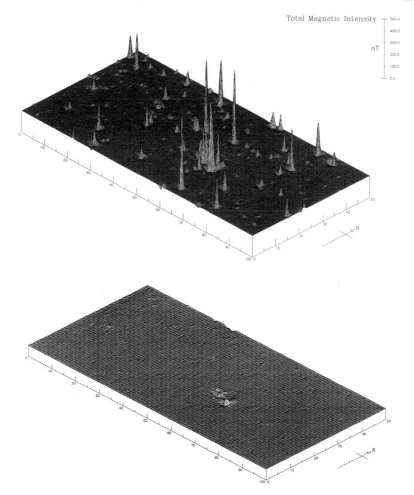

FIGURE 2.2   High-resolution magnetic survey for UXO detection

Unexploded ordnance (UXO) contamination exists on active and former military training and testing ranges. Environmental restoration of these sites to support future training and testing and return them to public use is a high priority. High-accuracy magnetic determinations can be particularly effective in the detection of ferrous UXO. If the type of ordnance is known, such surveys permit the areal location, depth, and approximate size of sub-surface UXO to be determined.

The top figure is from a high-resolution magnetic survey over a contaminated World War II artillery range. Data were collected with an automated survey system consisting of an array of optically pumped magnetometer sensors combined with a differential Global Positioning System, operated from an all-terrain vehicle. A similar survey (bottom) after the area had been cleared of ordnance produced a uniformly flat figure with the exception of residual rust flakes from other metallic debris. (Example courtesy of Geophysical Technology Limited, Armidale, Australia.)

CIVIL INFRASTRUCTURE

Many civil engineering projects require characterization of the shallow subsurface. Such projects include the design and construction of roads, airfields, bridges, dams, water supply and wastewater treatment facilities, housing, industrial and office buildings, tunnels, power plants, and safe storage facilities for wastes of all types.

In addition to design and construction, subsurface information is needed for the rehabilitation of existing underground infrastructure. A common application of noninvasive techniques is for locating existing underground utilities (e.g., telephone, gas, water, electric) and structures (see Plates 3 and 4). The National Transportation Safety Board (1997) cites the needs for proper use of geophysics in locating underground utilities before digging, excavating, or drilling, and for statistics on inadequate implementation of geophysical sensing. It also states that "a single pipeline accident has the potential to cause a catastrophic disaster that can injure hundreds of persons, affect thousands more, and cost millions of dollars in terms of property damage, loss of work opportunity, ecological damage, and insurance liability." Typically about 70 such events occur in the United States every year (National Transportation Safety Board, 1997).

Many geotechnical projects have traditionally relied on field penetration tests, in situ tests of various types, and laboratory tests on samples of varying quality and representation. However, noninvasive tests have been used increasingly in recent years because they often cost less, are relatively easy to conduct, and provide information not readily obtained by other means. In addition, noninvasive methods can test a much larger volume of the subsurface than traditional sampling or in situ testing approaches. These methods provide an excellent supplement than can limit the number of invasive methods used in most projects. A coordinated approach that combines invasive and noninvasive methods is likely to yield the most reliable site characterization.

Most infrastructure projects have several characterization objectives in common. At a minimum, geologists and engineers seek to know and understand the types of soil and rock materials and their stratigraphy, as well as the engineering properties of the different materials and the depth to groundwater. Construction in urban areas also requires information about existing underground works such as utilities, tunnels, and preexisting foundations. The engineering property requirements consist of five types: (1) volume change characteristics, so that settlements or heaves may be estimated; (2) strength, so that the stability of slopes, embankments, and excavations can be analyzed and the supporting capacities of foundations determined; (3) deformation characteristics, so that ground movements may be anticipated, dynamic response to earthquakes analyzed, and soil-structure interactions studied; (4) hydraulic conductivity properties (and in certain situations, thermal, electrical, and chemical conductivity) so that flow quantities can be estimated; and (5) the likelihood that these properties may change with time.

Current limitations of noninvasive methods for geotechnical applications include the inability to define boundaries and identify material types with sufficient accuracy, the inability to analyze small volumes or zones that may have a critical importance (e.g., failure to detect small-scale heterogeneity), and a lack of noninvasive methods for determining strength, volume change, and hydraulic conductivity properties (except as they might be deduced through correlations with material type). In addition, there is often a lack of unique interpretation from a given set of geophysical measurements.

HAZARDS

Noninvasive methods can play a critical role in characterizing certain natural hazards. Ground failure risks from natural hazards (e.g., surface manifestation of earthquakes, floods, landslides, and expansive or collapsing soils) require identification and mitigation to ensure public safety, as well as for reasons of economy. Knowledge of stratigraphy and engineering properties is essential for analysis of ground responses to forces of nature, such as gravity, earthquake ground motion, wind, and waves. Seismic methods are particularly well suited for evaluating the mechanical properties and interpreting ground behavior under dynamic loading.

Subsurface cavities are another type of hazard commonly associated with sudden ground failure. These cavities, which include natural sinkholes and caverns as well as human-made tunnels or subterranean chambers, must be properly located (see Figure 2.3). Sinkholes might have no surface expression until they breach the surface and cause considerable damage to engineering infrastructure. By knowing where cavities are, one can avoid building on them. In addition, knowledge of underground cavity distribution often gives information on the water flow network that such cavities can provide.

Conduits and caves can act as pipes, allowing contaminated groundwater to migrate rapidly over great distances. Some of the more troublesome groundwater contamination disasters have occurred in karst (limestone) aquifers where the existence or location of conduits was initially unrecognized. Structural engineering projects can also be severely impacted if there are large openings in underlying bedrock.

On a much more localized scale, noninvasive techniques (particularly GPR) can be used in road maintenance, particularly in monitoring asphalt pavement thickness and detecting air-filled voids or bridge deck delamination (NRC, 1998).

ARCHAEOLOGY

Recent federal legislation such as the Native American Graves Protection and Repatriation Act, the Archaeological Resources Protection Act, and the Na-

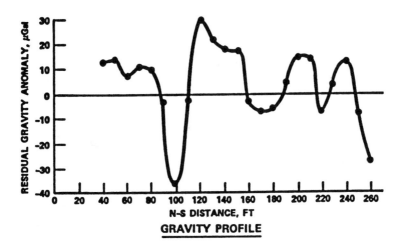

GRAVITY PROFILE

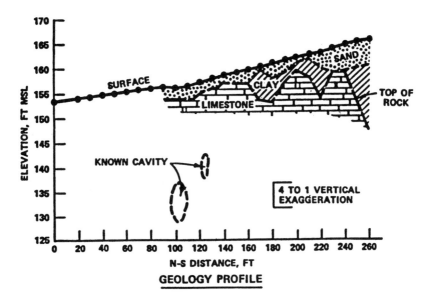

GEOLOGY PROFILE

FIGURE 2.3 Microgravity profile (top) and corresponding geological section (bottom) determined by closely spaced drilling. Known air-filled cavities passing under the profile line are shown in the geological section. The gravity anomaly profile indicates a negative anomaly over the cavities and positive and negative anomalies correlating to limestone pinnacles and clay-filled pockets, respectively. The negative anomaly over the cavities is a superposition of the effects of the cavities plus solution-enlarged porosity and fractures above and around the cavities. Adapted from Butler (1984).

tional Historic Preservation Act of 1966 mandate cultural resource assessments prior to construction or other activity that could endanger either known or undiscovered cultural artifacts.

At an archaeological site, the overall characterization objective is to find the artifacts and features. Specific characterization objectives include the direct detection of these objects and the detection of disturbed ground that indicates past human activity. Traditional archaeological field research involves invasive methods such as the careful digging of pits and trenches to find, extract, and document artifacts. The time and cost involved in these methods have increased interest in the use of noninvasive techniques, particularly geophysical methods, to map archaeological sites and plan the locations of invasive sampling. In addition, geophysical methods often allow archaeologists to detect and map patterns at sites that are often extremely difficult to detect and visualize from standard procedures. For example, Katsonopoulou and Soter (1996) used GPR in the exploration of ancient Helike. Some geophysical investigations of archaeological sites have received considerable public and popular-scientific media attention— for example, Lakshmanan and Montlucon's (1987) discovery of hidden chambers in the Great Pyramid at Giza, Egypt.

Because geophysical anomalies caused by archaeological artifacts and features are often small and subtle, the geophysical methods and survey procedures used often must be high resolution and precise. They generally must be multimethod, integrated investigations. Archaeological application requirements often stimulate innovative, cutting-edge developments in geophysical equipment, field procedures, and interpretation methods. The work by Butler et al. (1994) to locate the exact site of the Wright brother's 1910 hanger demonstrated this multimethod, integrated approach through its use of scanned period aerial photographs georeferenced to the geophysical survey maps and site facility maps (see Figure 2.4). Their work also showed that archaeological investigations do not always involve ancient or prehistoric objectives and that anomalies due to even relatively recent cultural site features can be very small in magnitude and subtle in expression.

BASIC SCIENCE

The upper tens of meters of the earth hold information critical to understanding many of the natural processes occurring within and on the earth. Studies of outcrops and of cores obtained through drilling have traditionally provided earth scientists with the samples used to investigate the properties and distributions of geological materials. These outcrops and samples are used to measure physical and chemical properties, to gain insights into the spatial distribution of these properties, and to develop models of the geological processes that formed the materials. For example, in studies of sedimentary deltaic environments, observed lithologic variation is used to develop models of the processes involved in the

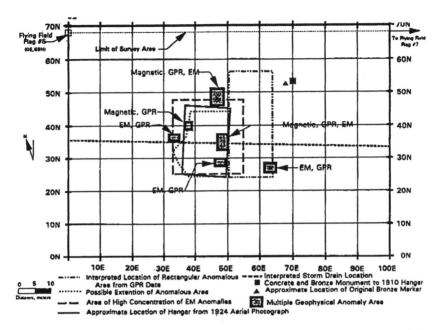

FIGURE 2.4   Wright Patterson Air Force Base plans to construct a replica of the 1910 Wright Brothers' hangar in the exact location of the original, especially for the centenary of powered flight in 2003.   The original hanger was razed in the late 1930s or early 1940s and no surface indication of its exact location exists. An archaeological geophysics investigation was conducted to locate any remaining signature or evidence of the old hangar foundation. This integrated geophysical anomaly map was constructed using surveys of GPR, magnetics, and frequency-domain electromagnetic induction, which were georeferenced to a digitized 1924 aerial photograph that showed the hangar.   Subsequent archaeological excavations confirmed the geophysical results by finding concentrations of period artifacts.   Figure from Butler and Simms, 1994.

transport and deposition of sediments. In areas of recent volcanism, outcrops provide information about the stages of a volcanic eruption. In areas adjacent to a fault zone, sampling provides information about the style of mechanical deformation within the earth.

For all of these examples and many others, noninvasive characterization of a three-dimensional volume of the subsurface can provide valuable information about geological properties and processes. Rather than being restricted to a two-dimensional exposed section of material at the surface or a one-dimensional sample of the earth obtained from drilling, noninvasive characterization provides a unique opportunity to study an undisturbed region of the earth. In addition, noninvasive technologies can provide continuous sampling of a region at a sampling density unlikely to be obtained through more expensive invasive technologies. One recent example of the use of noninvasive technologies for the advancement of basic science is the use of GPR to image the volcanic deposits of Santorini (Russell and Stasiak, 1997). The clear delineation of the basement rocks and the various layers (corresponding to stages of volcanic activity) either provide information about the volcanic process that could not be obtained from other sampling methods or help interpret one-dimensional sampling methods.

Even in situations where extensive information can be extracted from surface outcrops, noninvasive techniques can provide continuous, high-resolution coverage in the third dimension. Studies of sedimentary environments require a quantitative description of the spatial variability in hydraulic properties for modeling fluid flow in groundwater aquifers. Although detailed analyses of outcrops can provide direct measurements of variation in properties such as porosity and permeability, noninvasive techniques can characterize the three-dimensional spatial variability of a region. The use of noninvasive technologies to characterize the heterogeneity inherent in geological systems will contribute directly to characterization needs for many applications, and may provide basic information required to understand geological processes. Noninvasive technologies provide a way of imaging the earth and quantifying many earth processes.

As noninvasive measurement techniques become more accurate, a new level of complexity will probably be revealed in physical processes of rocks and soils. For example, observations of nonlinearity and anisotropy of physical properties might result from improved techniques and sources. Such observations would provide new basic scientific information on subsurface materials.

REFERENCES

Butler, D. K., 1984. Microgravimetric and gravity gradient techniques for detection of subsurface cavities, *Geophysics 49*(7), 1084-1096.

Butler, D. K., and J. E. Simms, 1994. Archaeological geophysics investigation of the Wright Brothers 1910 Hangar site, *Geoarchaeology 9*(6), 437-466.

Defense Science Board, 1998. Task Force Report on Unexploded Ordnance (UXO) Clearance, Active Range UXO Clearance, and Explosive Ordnance Disposal (EOD) Programs, Task Force Report to the Office of the Under Secretary of Defense (Acquisition and Technology), April 1998. www.acq.osd.mil/ens/esb/dsbfnlrpt.pdf.

Inter-Parliamentary Union, 1996. Resolution (20 September 1996) by the 96th Inter-Parliamentary Conference of the Inter-Parliamentary Union, held in Beijing, United Nations.

The Joint Unexploded Ordnance Clearance Steering Group, 1997. *Unexploded Ordnance Clearance: A Coordinated Approach to Requirements and Technology Development, Report to Congress*, Office of the Under Secretary of Defense (Acquisition and Technology), March 1997.

Katsonopoulou, D., and S. Soter, 1996. Ancient Helike in the light of recent discoveries, Archaeological Institute of America Annual Meeting, New York.

Lakshmanan, J., and J. Montlucon, 1987. Microgravity probes the Great Pyramid, *The Leading Edge 6*(1), 10-17.

National Research Council (NRC), 1994. *Alternatives for Ground Water Cleanup*, Water Science and Technology Board, National Academy Press, Washington, D.C.

NRC, 1998. *Ground Penetrating Radar for Evaluating Subsurface Conditions for Transportation Facilities*, Transportation Research Board (NCHRP Synthesis of Highway Practice, Report 255), Topic 26-08), Washington, D.C., 37 pp.

National Transportation Safety Board (NTSB), 1997. Protecting Public Safety Through Excavation Damage Prevention, Safety Study NTSB/SS-97/01, Washington, D.C., 106 pp.

Rivett, M. O, and J. A. Cherry, 1991. The effectiveness of soil gas surveys in the delineation of groundwater contamination: Controlled experiments at the Borden field site. In *Proceedings of the Conference on Petroleum Hydrocarbons and Organic Chemicals in Groundwater*, Houston, Texas, November 20-22, pp. 107-124.

Roberts, D. E., and G. R. T. Hudson, 1983. The Olympic Dam copper-uranium-gold deposit, Roxby Downs, South Australia, *Economic Geology 78*(5), 799-822.

Rumer, R. R., and J. K. Mitchell, eds., 1996. *Assessment of Barrier Containment Technologies: A Comprehensive Treatment for Environmental Remediation Applications*, NTIS Publication No. PB96-180583, 437 pp.

Russell, J. K., and M. V. Stasiak, 1997. Characterization of volcanic deposits with ground-penetrating radar, *Bulletin Volcanology 58*, 515-527.

Sternberg, B. K., 1993. Construction of a lined basin for tests of the high resolution subsurface imaging ellipticity system, EPRI (Electrical Power Research Institute) Final report on Research Project 2485-11.

U. S. Army Environmental Center (USAEC), 1994. Unexploded ordnance advanced technology demonstration program at Jefferson Proving Ground (Phase I), Report No. SFIM-AEC-ET-CR-94120, U.S. Army Environmental Center, Aberdeen Proving Ground, Maryland.

3

What Is Characterized?

As discussed in Chapter 2, characterization of the subsurface provides the information required for numerous applications from resource exploration to basic science. Although the applications and the motivations vary, in the broadest sense the specific characterization objectives often are similar. In most cases, information is required about the materials, their boundaries, and their properties (see Table 3.1); in many cases, knowledge is also needed about the physical, chemical, and biological processes in the subsurface and their variation in space and time.

PROPERTIES AND PROCESSES

Noninvasive determinations of subsurface properties and processes are indirect. Many properties are interpreted from measured perturbations in fields that are generated artificially or naturally. *Passive investigations* measure variations in naturally occurring fields (the earth's gravity, magnetic, electric, thermal, radiometric, stress, solar irradiation, and hydraulic fields). For example, perturbations in the earth's gravity field can be used to infer subsurface changes in the material density or the presence of voids. *Active investigations* use a source of energy that creates a known field, and measurements are made of the perturbations in this field or in the response of the earth to it. For example, seismic investigations use vibratory or explosive sources to propagate elastic waves and observe their travel times, wavelet changes, and scattering to describe the heterogeneity of the interior of the earth.

Many of the properties and most of the processes within the earth occur not in isolation but in relation to one another. Fluid flow through a porous material

TABLE 3.1   Example of Properties Often Needed for Characterization

Physical Properties	**Transport**—electrical, thermal or hydraulic conductivity, permeability, elastic attenuation **Storage**—dielectric permittivity, magnetic permeability, hydraulic storativity, elastic moduli **Strength**—mechanical, dielectric breakdown **Textural**—density, porosity, pore or grain size and shape distribution, water content **Morphological**—pore lining/bridging/blocking clays
Chemical Properties	Concentration, diffusion coefficient, reactivity, kinetics, solubility, mineralogy, phase
Biological Properties	Identity, abundance, diversity, ecology and overall physiological status and activity potential
Geological Properties	Stratigraphy, depth/thickness, dip/strike/azimuth, fracture presence/concentration/orientation, state of stress, migration pathways, water table depth

often will create an electrical current flow that generates a voltage called a streaming potential. A measurement of streaming potential sometimes can be used to locate flowing water (e.g., dam leaks). Many transport properties are dominated by the presence of water-filling pore spaces, which causes positive correlative behavior (or response) between conduction properties and environmental factors such as rainfall or freeze-thaw. Not all desired physical, chemical, and biological properties and processes can be determined noninvasively. Some have been measured for centuries (e.g., the earth's magnetic and gravity fields), whereas others are still on the horizon (e.g., biological activity).

Most subsurface physical processes involve either movement or storage of energy or mass; they can be described by either the diffusion or wave propagation equations. Heat flow, induced electrical current flow, and hydraulic fluid flow are all processes described by the diffusion equation, with the diffusion coefficient describing the property of conductivity. Mechanical particle movement and the coupled electromagnetic field behavior are described by the equations of wave propagation. The attenuation of the propagating wave is related to energy loss (and energy transport), whereas the velocity of propagation is related to the ability of the material to store energy.

A good deal of characterization has simply been anomaly detection (e.g., detecting where things differ from normal background or from the surface materials). From such measurements, the location and size of an anomaly can be determined. Detection of anisotropy (measurements in different directions giving different values for the same property) is especially important in systems dealing with fracture-dominated fluid flow. Determination of connectivity is important in mining clay and coal seams and environmental cleanup. Inadequate ability to describe and understand heterogeneity is probably the single largest reason for the failure of groundwater cleanup methods at hazardous waste sites. Measurements made at different scales are known to produce different responses. For example, the mechanical strength of a rock is inversely related to the size of the sample measured, and the hydraulic conductivity of fractured rock usually increases with the size of the sample measured. Such behavior often is not properly taken into account when such measurements are transferred from field surveys to site characterization models.

Many properties and processes are known to change with time, and knowing when a measurement was performed can be vital to its interpretation. This temporal perspective is especially important with regard to seasonal, freeze-thaw, and wet-dry variations that can affect not only properties but processes (e.g., erosion, stream flow, landslides, sinkholes, frost heaving, swelling clay). Contaminant plumes can move through the subsurface for long periods and can be disturbed or remobilized by site remediation activities. Stresses can build up over long periods and be released over shorter periods, as in earthquakes. Water tables rise and fall with tidal events, water well pumping, and climate changes.

EXAMPLES OF CHARACTERIZATION

Some selected examples of characterization follow. The discussion of each example focuses on a specific characterization objective (which might be common to many applications) and reviews the noninvasive techniques that can be used.

Geological Characterization

A site's geology defines the overall framework within which study of the subsurface environment is carried out. Questions relating to, for example, the occurrence and movement of groundwater, geotechnical investigations, resource exploration, the migration of chemical contaminants, and the subsurface environment's microbiology, must all be posed in the context of the site's geology. The nature and extent of the related physical, chemical, and biological processes are constrained by the structure and lithology of the bedrock and overlying surficial materials. All aspects of site characterization and remedial investigations are influenced by the geological setting.

Lithology

The different physical properties of different lithologies make it possible to obtain information about them from geophysical measurements. Commonly used measurements include differences in seismic velocity, electrical resistivity, and dielectric permittivity. In most cases there is not a unique relationship between a measured physical property and lithology; however, the combined use of different noninvasive techniques to measure complementary properties can help determine and analyze a site's lithology.

Different rock types, each with a characteristic mineralogy and geochemistry, react differently with water, solutes, suspended solids, and microorganisms. Often these reactions are poorly understood. Rock types also have typical physical characteristics or engineering properties and, thus, compact and deform in particular ways. In addition, there is a strong correlation between lithology and the occurrence of certain types of resources.

Detailed lithological maps can help evaluate the impact of aquifer contamination and various remediation schemes. The likelihood of migration of a dissolved contaminant in groundwater, for example, is influenced by adsorption to mineral surfaces, the dissolution or precipitation reactions of minerals, and oxidation-reduction reactions, which are often mediated by microorganisms. The reactions possible in a given aquifer are defined largely by the aquifer's lithology. Further, certain hydraulic properties may be characteristic of certain rock types.

Knowledge of lithology is also essential for engineering and construction in the subsurface. Lithological characteristics (e.g., hard rock, soft rock, intact rock, jointed rock) greatly affect such things as a site's suitability for foundation support, applicable methods for excavation, and groundwater flow conditions.

Some lithologies are especially important to identify. Limestone and other soluble rock types may be extensively dissolved at depth, creating secondary porosity and permeability. Being heterogeneous in their distribution, such subsurface conduits in limestone are difficult to map, though certain noninvasive techniques can detect large openings in shallow bedrock (see Figure 2.3 using a microgravity method).

Shale and clay are important to site characterization for engineering and environmental applications. Low-permeability shale layers that are not fractured can confine transmissive sandstone aquifers, trap migrating hydrocarbons, or prevent migration of landfill leachate. Exact knowledge of their location and continuity in the subsurface is critical to properly assessing their role in site or regional hydrogeology. Clay can occur dispersed as lenses within another lithology. For instance, clay lenses in a sandy aquifer can create perched water table conditions that could confound our understanding of flow conditions. Clay lenses also can act as reservoirs of immobile groundwater into which contaminants can diffuse and be retained in an aquifer undergoing traditional pump-and-treat remediation. The ability to recognize relatively small clay layers or lenses within an aquifer system would improve our ability to develop and protect groundwater resources. The presence of certain clays is also of concern in foundation design because it can lead to extensive settlement or heave (e.g., Chleborad et al., 1996).

Structure and Stratigraphy

Porosity and hydraulic conductivity set the broad constraints on fluid migration in the subsurface, an important issue in environmental and engineering studies. These properties depend on structural features such as faults, fractures, folds, and lithological contacts (see Figure 3.1). Further, the actual location of groundwater, contaminants, ore deposits, and planes of weakness for engineering purposes may be constrained by subsurface structural features.

Fractures as well as contacts between different lithologies are often pathways for groundwater flow. Some rock types (primarily poorly cemented sandstone) have significant porosity and permeability, but most rock types, whether sedimentary, igneous, or metamorphic, do not. Ground water occurrence and movement in such rocks is almost entirely controlled by structural features. Bedding planes in sedimentary sequences and fractures in sedimentary, igneous, and metamorphic rocks may offer significant conduits for fluid migration.

Structural features largely control communication among various water-bearing units as well. Even in a simple layer-cake sedimentary sequence (e.g., a water-saturated sandstone confined by low-transmissivity, clay-rich shales), assessing the fate of contaminants is difficult, if not impossible, without understanding cross-strata transport pathways. A confining layer can be breached by flow along faults and fractures, which can dramatically influence predictions about contaminant containment (see Figure 3.5). Many of the groundwater contamination sites that require restoration today resulted from mistaken presumptions about the integrity of engineered or geological barriers to fluid flow (National Research Council, 1984).

Noninvasive detection of these structural features (faults, fractures, folds, lithologic contacts) relies on the existence of a contrast in properties across these features or a unique response associated with them. Lithologies on either side of a feature, can have significantly different physical properties such as seismic velocity, dielectric constant, and electrical resistivity. Given that these features are often continuous over meters to tens of meters or kilometers, it is generally possible to locate such features with existing technology if the conditions at the site are appropriate. One example of mapping a lithological contact—the top of the bedrock—is given in Davis and Annan (1989), where ground penetrating radar (GPR) was used to image the interface between the granodioritic bedrock and overlying fine sands. The contrast in dielectric constant coupled with the continuity of the contrast made this an ideal target for GPR.

The noninvasive technologies can produce high-quality images of the near-surface structure and stratigraphy; however, their success can be highly variable. There can be a large influence of the very near surface on most noninvasive methods. For example, weathering within the vadose (or water-unsaturated) zone can produce submeter-scale heterogeneities in physical properties that cause significant problems with seismic reflection data; overcoming these "statics" re-

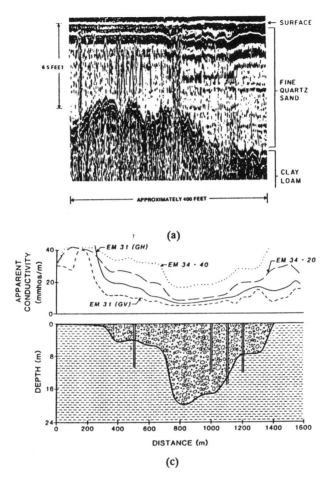

FIGURE 3.1 Examples of stratigraphic interpretations using subsurface geophysical surveys: (a) ground penetrating radar (from Benson et al., 1982); (b) delineating a bedrock channel by seismic reflection (from Benson, 1991); (c) relationship of EM

quires mixing of data that can lose resolution. In the use of GPR the most common limiting problem is the occurrence of clays, with a high electrical conductivity (>30 mS/m) that prevents the penetration of radar signals. The groundwater table can have a similar limiting effect if the conductivity of the water is high.

Fractures

Understanding the presence, distribution, and connectiveness of fractures is critical to site characterization. Fractures play a fundamental role in where and

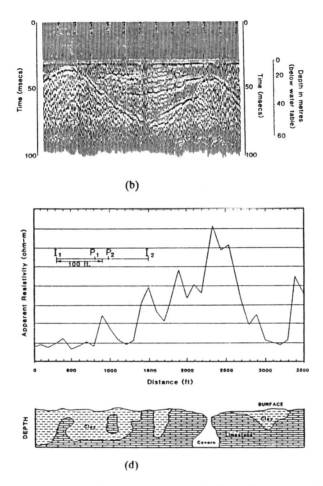

(b)

(d)

conductivity data and a sand and gravel channel (from Hoekstra and Hoekstra, 1991); and (d) electrical resistivity profile of karst terrain (from Hoekstra and Hoekstra, 1991). (Figure adapted from Cohen and Mercer, 1993).

how rapidly fluids can move through the subsurface and to the surface. A recent National Research Council report (NRC, 1996) provides a comprehensive review of research on techniques and approaches to fracture characterization and fluid flow in rock fractures.

Fracture detection depends on detecting physical property change across the fracture or within the fracture itself (see Figure 3.2). In addition to observing topographic expression using images and photographs, various remote sensing methods (including multispectral reflectance, imaging spectroscopy, thermal in-

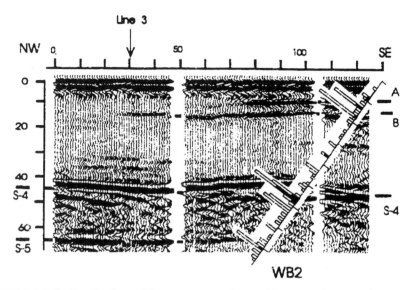

FIGURE 3.2 Semihorizontal fracture zones observed by ground penetrating radar along a profile measured on granitic outcrops at the Underground Research Laboratory, Manitoba, Canada, showing distribution of fractures along borehole WB2. Reflectors S-4 and S-5, seen at depths of 40 to 50 m and 65 m, respectively, are verified by increased fracture frequency observed in the slanted borehole. (From Holloway et al., 1992).

frared, and radar) have been used to detect juxtaposed lithologic contrasts at the surface. Thermal infrared images also have been used to infer fractures where moisture content differences in soil cause associated surface temperature changes. Detecting fractures beneath the surface often depends on observing contrasts in physical properties such as dielectric constant, electrical conductivity, P-wave seismic velocity and attenuation, magnetic susceptibility, and density—all of which can be related to interconnected void space or moisture content of the fracture zone. High spatial resolution is required for both location and detection of fractures. Frequently used methods for detailed work have been GPR (see Figure 3.2) and seismology. Resistivity surveys and detailed magnetic surveys also have had limited success. Resistivity soundings repeated over a range of azimuths at one location often can indicate the gross vertical fracture directions (see Figure 3.3). Generally, remote sensing methods lack the detailed follow-up work to verify results.

The connectedness of fractures is important to characterization because these connections affect whether and where fluids can flow as well as the flow rates. Hydraulically significant fractures may comprise only a small fraction of the total fractures present. Detailed three-dimensional mapping of properties (at scales that depend on the problem) is required to evaluate connectedness between fractures. Fractures may vary in length from hand specimen size to kilometers, with widths generally a couple of orders of magnitude less. Their presence at a site may be the source of anisotropy in an otherwise isotropic background. Because fractures are conduits for fluids, anomalous mineralization may occur with them. Where these minerals outcrop, they may be detected by imaging spectroscopy. If the minerals produce an electrical conductivity contrast, this can provide three-dimensional information about the fracture. In almost all cases, surface geophysical methods cannot characterize completely a fractured rock site because the fractures that have flow cannot be separated from fractures without flow. To characterize such sites, hydraulic testing and borehole geophysical methods usually are required.

Heterogeneity

Spatial heterogeneities in the physical properties of rock units prevent complete characterization of subsurface rock formations from observations made in outcrops or in cores. In environmental and engineering studies, properties of

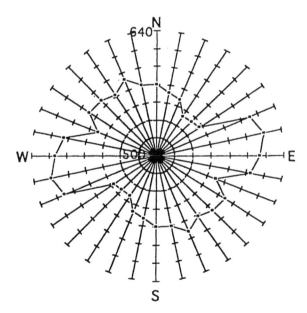

FIGURE 3.3 Resistivity measurements made in 16 different directions define a resistivity ellipse whose major axis is aligned with the fracture orientation. This example, from an open-pit quarry in southern Indiana, demonstrates that the dominant fracture direction is east-west. (From Cohn and Rudman, 1995.)

interest, such as porosity, hydraulic conductivity, and chemical or mineralogical composition might vary over short distances within a single geological unit. No reliable mathematical model for interpolating between observations exists. Most mapping of lithology is done by assuming continuity between observation points. Yet a single important discontinuity in material properties may dictate the fate and transport of contaminants or the stability of a rock slope. Many site remediation failures result from inadequate characterization of site heterogeneity (EPA, 1992). An ability to more fully describe the location and character of heterogeneities throughout an aquifer would yield a better description of hydraulic, geochemical, and biological responses to contamination or remediation.

The importance of minor geological details in geotechnical engineering is well known (e.g., Terzaghi, 1929). Thin clay layers may serve as slip surfaces, impairing the stability of both natural slopes and excavations. Sand lenses may act both as drains or sources of artesian pressure and water flow into an area, depending on the regional hydrogeology. The natural heterogeneity of sand and gravel deposits is the source of nonuniform settlements and uncertainties about resistance to liquefaction during earthquakes.

The key to effectively describing the subsurface's heterogeneous nature is most likely the integration of different types of information at different scales. Although noninvasive techniques can determine large-scale lithologic units, high-resolution, often invasive, measurements are required to detect meter- or submeter-scale changes in rock and/or fluid properties. There is considerable interest in the use of GPR to noninvasively image this small-scale spatial variability. Very closely spaced electrical and electromagnetic sounding techniques also have the potential to provide increased lateral resolution (see Figure 3.4). In addition, arrays of sensors and multicomponent measurements may provide more detail on the spatial variations in resistivity and electrical polarization.

Fluids

Subsurface fluids play a large role in resource recovery and storage, environmental protection and remediation, and civil engineering projects. In the unsaturated (or vadose) zone above the water table, there is generally a two-phase fluid system consisting of an aqueous phase and a gaseous phase. In areas contaminated with organic chemicals, a third nonaqueous-phase liquid (NAPL) may also be present. (The most frequently encountered NAPL contaminants are organic solvents and hydrocarbon fuels.) The aqueous phase may contain various dissolved natural and human-made constituents, such as salts, pesticides, and organic chemicals. Soil gas is primarily air, but also contains on the order of 1 weight percent water vapor and may contain trace amounts of organic chemical vapors as well as noncondensable gases such as CO_2 and radon. Beneath the water table, the gaseous phase is usually unimportant, and there is a single aque-

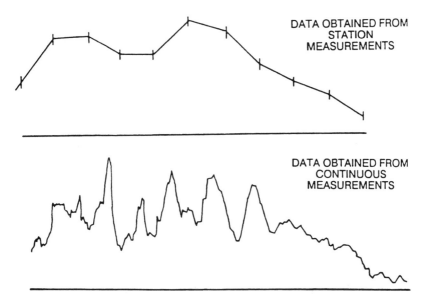

DATA OBTAINED FROM
STATION
MEASUREMENTS

DATA OBTAINED FROM
CONTINUOUS
MEASUREMENTS

FIGURE 3.4   Comparison of station and continuous surface EM conductivity measurements made along the same transect. The electrical conductivity peaks are due to fractures in gypsum bedrock. (From Benson et al., 1982.)

ous phase or a two-phase (aqueous and NAPL) system. The interfaces between these fluid phases are often biologically active.

Generally speaking, all aspects of the presence and behavior of fluids in the subsurface are of interest—their distribution (e.g., Figure 3.5) and composition, their rates of migration, and the hydraulic properties of the subsurface media. Hydraulic properties include permeability, porosity, and when multiple fluid phases are present, relative permeability and capillary pressure characteristics. Hydraulic parameters tend to vary spatially; they can also depend on the scale of investigation. The desired level of detail for characterizing these parameters depends strongly on the engineering or remediation applications. Demands on spatial resolution and identification of minor fluid components tend to be greatest in the area of contaminant hydrology. Noninvasive techniques are usually incapable of unambiguously resolving site characterization needs relating to fluids, but they can contribute valuable information, especially when used in conjunction with a minimum amount of invasive methods for providing "ground truth."

Common site characterization tasks include two that are identified as part of geological characterization: the location of permeable features and the location of features with low permeability such as clay layers. In addition, common charac-

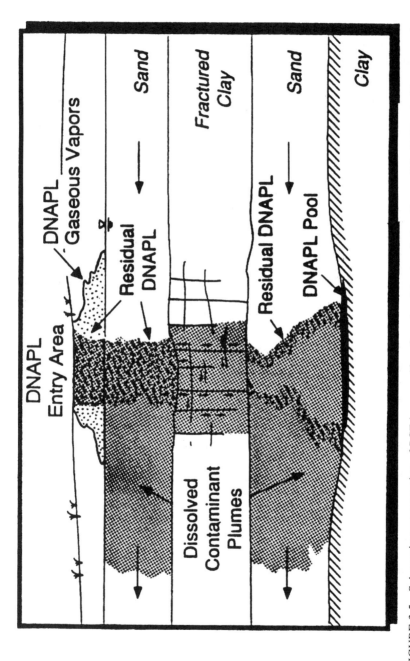

FIGURE 3.5   Schematic representation of PCE in an aquifer of sand and fractured clay. Some of the PCE volatilizes, some is trapped as a residual in soil pores, some migrates into the fractures, and some pools on the clay layers (from Cohen and Mercer, 1993).

terization tasks specific to addressing the distribution and migration of fluids include the depth to the water table and the chemical composition of the fluids. For some applications it is sufficient to know changes in fluid distribution over time rather than the current distribution of fluids.

Depth to the Water Table

Knowing the location of the water table is essential for almost every environmental, resource recovery, and engineering application. There are significant contrasts in transport properties, chemical and microbiological reactions, and strength and deformation properties between the unsaturated vadose zone and the water-saturated zone.

The water table is an interface across which there may be a change in several physical properties (electrical conductivity, seismic wave velocity, dielectric constant), making it a viable target for detection with geophysical techniques. However, in some situations (e.g., coarse-grained sands and gravels), the contrast in physical properties is between the saturated and the unsaturated zone, so geophysical techniques may locate the top of the saturated zone, which might be different from the true water table. Complications in detecting this interface arise when air is trapped below the "water table" due to annual fluctuations in the level.

Geophysical methods commonly used include direct current (dc) resistivity, time- and frequency-domain electromagnetic soundings, seismic refraction, and GPR. Each of these methods, whether model based (e.g., dc resistivity) or image based (e.g., GPR), requires ancillary data—often a by-product of data processing (e.g., radar wave propagation velocity) or from drill holes—for complete interpretation. In addition to geophysical detection, increased biological activity at the water table may cause oxygen depletion, changes in pH and eH, production of biomass, specific mineral accumulations, and gas production (methane, CO_2, dissolved hydrogen).

Fluid Composition

Knowledge of the chemical composition of fluids in the subsurface often is required to assess groundwater quality, to track the movement of contaminants, and to monitor containment remediation. Fluid composition can affect the physical, chemical, and biological properties of these confining geological or soil units in ways that allow remote detection of the fluid's composition. Characterization involves assessing the nature and amount of dissolved and suspended inorganic and organic constituents.

In some cases, it is possible to directly detect the contaminant using electromagnetic methods. For example, recognizing electrically conductive water in the near surface (see Plate 5) caused by chloride ions from salt water is a relatively easy procedure using commercially available equipment and routine geophysical interpretation procedures. Similarly, chloride ions in soils from improper disposal of water co-produced from petroleum production can be detected easily. The signal levels associated with electrically conductive contaminants are often one to two orders of magnitude higher than background levels, which leads to a high degree of confidence (see Plate 6). The distribution of such near-surface contaminants often can be modeled in three dimensions (Danbom, 1995). With such a three-dimensional model, a limited direct sampling program could confirm and calibrate the electrical geophysical anomalies.

Many contaminants, such as petroleum hydrocarbons, are electrically insulative and, therefore, much more difficult to detect. However, Benson et al. (1997) provide an example of successfully detecting petroleum hydrocarbons using the offset sounding procedure variant in dc resistivity.

Immiscible fluids such as gasoline and chlorinated solvents can sometimes be found using complex resistivity (induced polarization) measurements to detect electrochemical reactions exhibited by these solvents in the presence of clay minerals.

Dissolved and immiscible organic contaminants remain virtually impossible to detect noninvasively; this vexing environmental problem is an opportunity for continued research. Under certain circumstances, nonconductive organic contaminants can be detected using GPR, which detects contrasts in the dielectric constants between materials such as pore water and organic compounds. An experimentally controlled spill of perchloroethylene (PCE), a dense nonaqueous-phase liquid (DNAPL), was successfully monitored using GPR and other techniques (Sander et al., 1992; Greenhouse et al., 1993). This study points out the need for time-differential measurements to remove background effects and allow the detection of small dielectric changes. The technique may be most useful for monitoring contaminant movement during remediation efforts.

Noninvasive geophysical techniques determine subsurface fluid distributions by finding a contrast in physical properties. A fundamental difficulty arises from the fact that geological media are often heterogeneous for a range of scales; single-method geophysical measurements cannot establish whether observed property variations are due to nonuniform fluid distributions or to formation heterogeneities. This nonuniqueness of the interpretation is reduced or eliminated if diverse data sets are available and if data can be collected over time to monitor changes associated with the movement of the fluid.

Increased biological activity often is found at the boundary of contaminant plumes. Evidence for this activity can be found in decreased concentrations of electron acceptors such as oxygen, nitrate, and sulfate, and in increased production of ferrous iron minerals and methane. Noninvasive detection of such microbial activity is not possible now, but is very desirable—hence, another research need. Minimally invasive sensing of microbial activity is possible through soil-gas surveys.

Biology

A wide range of organisms inhabit the soil and subsurface. More complex eukaryotic biota such as plant roots, earthworms, nematodes, insect larvae, and soil algae are limited to the upper regions of biologically active soil (Killham, 1994); simpler life forms such as bacteria, fungi, protozoa (and probably viruses) extend into deeper regions of the subsurface (Ghiorse and Wilson, 1988; Madsen and Ghiorse, 1993; Frederickson and Onstott, 1996; Amy and Haldeman, 1997; Ghiorse, 1997).

The properties of the biota of most interest to site characterization biologists may be the most difficult to determine noninvasively. The identity, abundance, diversity, and ecology of the resident organisms, as well as their overall physiological status, are the most important general properties to assess. Some of these properties can be assessed by minimally invasive methods such as soil-gas analysis and selective culturing techniques. Noninvasive remote sensing technology shows some promise in such assessments, but until more research is done to develop other methods, characterization of site biology will still depend to a large degree on analysis of samples obtained by invasive methods.

There is a possibility that some biologically mediated environmental properties might be detected by noninvasive or minimally invasive geophysical techniques. These properties could be targeted to indicate near-surface biological activity.

Buried Objects

The location of buried objects is a relatively common objective in subsurface and site characterization. The information required about the object usually includes the following:

- Where is it (lateral position)?
- How deep is it (vertical position)?
- How large is it?
- What is around it (context)?
- What shape is it?
- What is its composition (metal, plastic, void)?
- What is it (pipe, bomb, drum, etc.)?

The specific set of parameters (physical, chemical, and biological) that need to be measured at a site to characterize buried objects depends on the defined target of interest and the host medium in which it is buried. The measurements must also take into account any sources of noise or interference. If the goal is to detect the presence of the object itself, the set of crucial parameters is determined by the contrast between the properties of the object and the medium in which it is buried.

(In addition to considering the initial state of the object at the time of burial, investigators must consider the possibility that there can be time-dependent changes in the object and the geological background due to processes such as weathering or corrosion.) These can produce distinct physical, chemical, and biological changes that can be monitored and used in locating and identifying the object. The detection of an object may also rely on more indirect measurements. One common example is the detection of the disturbed ground surrounding a buried object.

To review the parameters used in the location of buried objects, it is convenient to divide the topic into metallic and nonmetallic materials. Location of underground cavities and voids is also treated in this section, because many of the principles are similar.

Metallic Objects

Metallic objects, which include buried drums, underground storage tanks, well casing, metal pipes, and UXO (see Figure 2.2), can range in size from millimeters to meters and can be buried at depths up to 10 m.

Given present geophysical techniques, the most useful physical property in terms of detection is the high electrical conductivity and magnetic permeability of these objects. Electrical conductivity can be measured remotely using electromagnetic methods. Adaptations of these methods are hand-held terrain conductivity meters, trolley-mounted transient electromagnetic gradiometers, and metal detectors used by the utility industry in locating underground cables and also used by "treasure hunters" (see Box 3.1). There are limitations in the use of any of these methods with respect to the accuracy with which the size and location of the object can be determined. An additional limitation is that near-surface anomalies can mask the presence of a deeper target.

A buried ferromagnetic object will also exhibit a magnetic anomaly that can be modeled to locate the object. The magnetic anomaly will have an induced component (proportional to the earth's magnetic field) as well as a permanent "remanent" component. However, magnetic properties (as well as electrical conductivity) can change with time if oxidation to nonmagnetic oxides occurs, resulting in noticeable difference between "new" objects and rusted objects. Also, as with other potential-field methods, other material distributions sometimes found in the subsurface can produce similar anomalies.

Metallic (and nonmetallic) objects in the subsurface will interact with high-frequency electromagnetic waves in such a way as to cause diffraction hyperbolas in unprocessed GPR data. These distinct patterns in GPR data often are used to locate buried objects.

It is often more feasible to detect the disturbed zone around the buried object than the object itself. The disturbed zone may differ from the surrounding region in its density, dielectric constant, and electrical conductivity. The small-scale

Color Plates

 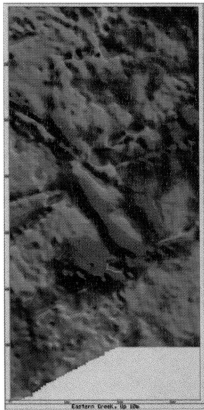

Magnetic data collected with a hand-held total-field magnetometer with resolution of 0.02 nT on traverses recorded with the sensor 1 m above ground with a sample interval of 0.5 m and a line spacing of 10 m, over an area 700 m by 1400 m. The data show a wealth of geological detail, containing shear zones, very thin dikes (<1 m), and a reverse magnetized plug.

Same area, with data collected at an elevation of 10 m from a helicopter-borne, dual-sensor system with laser elevation meter. The sensors are transverse to the aircraft, giving a 10-m data line spacing with two survey lines per flight line. This helimag system closely meets the ground specifications, but the thinnest of the dikes have slipped out of view. The helimag data cost about one-quarter to one-third as much as the hand-held data.

PLATE 1   An application of high-resolution magnetics in coal exploration is shown below. The inherent resolution of potential field geophysical techniques such as magnetics depends on the distance from the sensor to the causative source. (Data courtesy of Newlands Coal and Geophysical Research Institute, Armidale, NSW, Australia.)

This photograph shows a lined basin constructed at the University of Arizona's Avra Valley Geophysical Test Site. The basin is 30 m by 30 m by 5 m deep. The entire basin was lined with high-density polyethelene; drain pipes were placed in the bottom and the basin refilled with native soil. This test site allows a closed system for injection and retrieval of fluids. During the summer of 1992, 24,170 liters of water were injected along a 1-m by 25-m strip at the center of the basin.

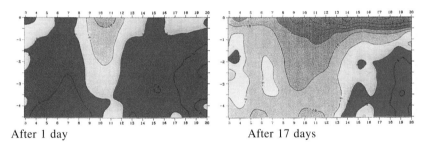

After 1 day   After 17 days

    Difference in electrical resistivity of the ground between the beginning (1 day) of the injection of a fluid and after 17 days. The small blue region (more negative than 10 ohm-m) in the left panel shows the location of the plume of injected water. After 17 days (right panel), the blue area has increased in depth and spread out. These data were collected with an electromagnetic sounding system. A long-line source was oriented parallel and offset 10 ohm-m from the injection region. The receiver line was perpendicular to the line source and the injection region. The scales are in meters. There was a close correspondence between these images and those based on 25 electric well-log and neutron probe measurements within the test basin. Such measurements make it possible to monitor and map the flow of fluids over time. From Sternberg (1993).

PLATE 2   Monitoring an underground plume with electromagnetic methods.

PLATE 3   Time-domain electromagnetics at Stanford Test Site. Several new time-domain electromagnetic (TEM) instruments have been developed to satisfy requirements of the environmental market. These instruments are based on techniques developed for the mineral exploration industry over the past two decades, specifically designed to discriminate between moderately conductive earth materials and more conductive metallic targets and, perhaps more importantly, to be more portable and less expensive than their exploration counterparts. The instrument is optimized to detect moderate-sized metallic conductors at depths of 1 m. Newer instruments are being designed to discriminate between ferrous and nonferrous materials, with better depth resolution.

The example below is from data gathered with a trolley-mounted TEM gradiometer system (Geonics EM 61) at Stanford University's environmental test site, which simulates many of the buried waste situations encountered in environmental assessments. The TEM instrument detected all of the known buried metallic objects as well as several unknown objects and clearly shows two buried pipes. A void is detected in the lower center of the image, evidenced by a subtle depression in the background. (Example courtesy of Geonics Limited, Missisauga, Canada.)

← North

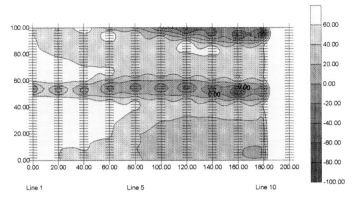

Line 1   Line 5   Line 10

Map view of the route of a buried pipeline as indicated by data collected with an induction-type, ground conductivity meter (Geonics EM 61). The pipeline, of steel construction, is buried about 5 feet. The anomalous conductivity at the upper right of the figure is due to reinforced concrete at the surface. The horizontal contouring in the center of the plot is an example of poor practice. The "bulls-eyes" that coincide with measurement points (to a lesser extent the same applies to the contours at the right near surface) are artifacts of an inadequate contouring software package. Line spacing 20 feet; station spacing 2 feet; conductivity millisiemens per meter; and contour interval is 20 mS/m. North is to the left.

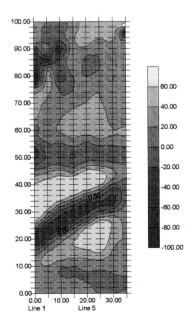

Line 1   Line 5

Map view of a different location showing a previously unknown pipeline (lower left to upper right) at an angle to the main pipeline as above (horizontally across the top). It was found to be another pipeline of a previous vintage and purpose that had not been removed. Line spacing is 5 feet; all other details are the same as the top figure. North is to the left.

PLATE 4   Using ground conductivity in locating buried pipelines.

Interpreted Resistivity Depth=1m

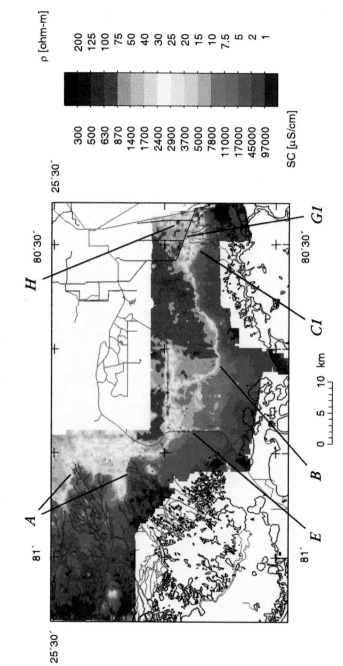

PLATE 5 Resistivity values at 1-m depth interpreted from a helicopter electromagnetic survey in the Everglades National Park, Florida; area covered was 1036 km². Coastlines and shores (black), rivers (magenta), canals (blue), and roads (red) are shown. The color bar shows interpreted formation resistivity on the right and estimated water quality (specific conductance) on the left, based on well-log correlations. Features shown are (A) diffuse freshwater-saltwater interface in Shark River Slough caused by tidal flow in drainages; (B) sharp interface in Taylor Slough; (C1) effect of near surface, freshwater recharge; (E) resistivity contrast produced by roadway blocking surface water flow; (G1) elevated near-surface resistivity due to flow from C-111 canal. Figure courtesy of D. V. Fitterman; see also Fitterman and Deszcz-Pan, 1998.

Photograph shows a survey being conducted at a site at a radioactive waste management acid pit at the Idaho National Engineering Laboratory. The site had been used
for dumping acid that contained radioactive wastes and other contaminants. This
was an operational survey to provide information for remediation of the site, and the
precise location of the wastes were not well known.

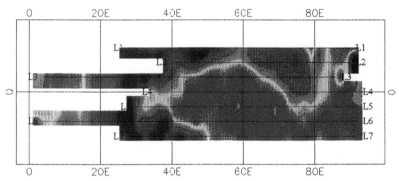

Plan map showing the distribution of subsurface resistivities based on ellipticity
measurement at a frequency of 62 kHz, which corresponds with a depth of about 2
to 2.5 ohm-m (line spacing was 4 m; measurement spacing along each line was 2
m). Data were collected with a coil spacing of 8 m. The red color (corresponding to
low electrical resistivities, of the order of 25(ohm-m) in the center of the map shows
the location of the most heavily contaminated soil. The blue color (of the order of 40
m) shows background soil response. The red color on the far left shows the location
of solid waste in an adjacent disposal cell. The red color on the far right shows the
location of buried utilities beneath a road. Other frequencies were used to map the
contaminant concentration at various depths. The soils at this site are far too conductive for ground penetrating (GPR) methods to be effectively used.

PLATE 6   Mapping contaminated soils (from Sternberg, 1997).

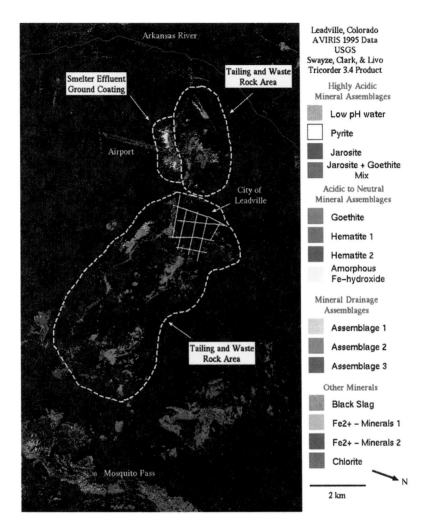

PLATE 7   Leadville iron-bearing mineral map. Map of the mineral distribution of
the waste rock and tailings piles at the California Gulch Superfund site near Leadville,
Colorado (130 km southwest of Denver). This map was produced by the U.S. Geological Survey for the U.S. Bureau of Reclamation and U.S. Environmental protection Agency using the NASA Jet Propulsion Laboratory Airborne Visible/Infrared
Imaging Spectrometer (AVIRIS). Each color identifies iron-bearing minerals in each
17×17 m^2 area pixel on the ground. Blue colors show minerals that cause acid mine
drainage high in dissolved metals such as cadmium, zinc, and lead. Areas in green
have minerals that are more neutral but still of concern. Other colors represent
minerals not contributing to water contamination. No iron-bearing minerals were
found in areas shown in black. Area shown is 10.5 km wide by 17 km long. North is
toward the lower right of the image.

> **BOX 3.1**
> **Treasure Hunters**
>
> Metal detectors respond to the contrast in electrical conductivity between a buried metal object and the ground. There are various types of metal detectors. With a two-coil system, a transmitter coil generates an alternating magnetic field around itself; this field is measured with a null-coupled or "balanced" receiver coil, oriented perpendicularly to the transmitter. If a metal object is encountered, eddy currents are generated that interact with the transmitter field to upset the original balanced condition; when this occurs, the instrument responds. The "treasure hunter"-type metal detectors often combine the transmitter and receiver functions in one coil, which responds to the field emanating from the object in different ways. Typical metal detectors have a relatively shallow range of operation; their response to a given object decreases at the rate of the target's depth to the sixth power ($1/D^6$). Small objects may be found to a depths of just up to a meter, whereas larger objects (e.g., 55-gallon drums) might be detected to depths of a few meters; these depths are dependent on many factors such as the size of the instrument's primary coil, coil separation, receiver sensitivity, the contrast in electrical conductivity, and the volume of the metal object.

structure will also be disrupted in the zone, which can produce a "jumbled" appearance in the GPR or high-resolution magnetic response from the area (see Figure 3.6).

Nonmetallic Objects

Nonmetallic objects of interest in site characterization include containers, pipes, UXO, and other waste. These objects commonly range in size from millimeters to meters and are buried at depths up to 10 m. Noninvasively detectable physical properties of nonmetallic objects include electrical conductivity, density, dielectric permittivity, and seismic velocity.

The detection of nonmetallic objects using electrical conductivity is possible only when there is a contrast with the background material. However, it is difficult to detect a resistive object within a conductive medium using electromagnetics. There is currently much interest in the location of nonmetallic objects using GPR (e.g., Bradford et al., 1996) to detect the contrast in electrical and dielectric properties between the objects and the background. High-frequency antennae, with theoretical resolution on the order of centimeters, could potentially be very useful for detecting small objects such as pipes.

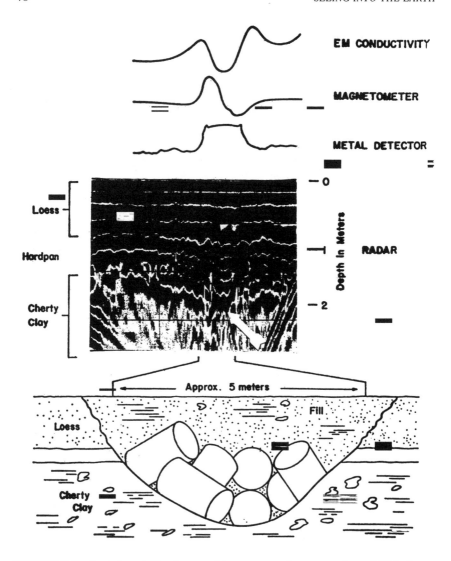

FIGURE 3.6   Buried metallic drums with representative magnetic and EM signatures; GPR signals show disturbed ground and surrounding stratigraphy. (After Benson and Glaccum, 1980.)

Cavities

It is important to locate subsurface cavities in karst areas prior to building or road construction in order to avoid potential future collapse (Franklin et al., 1981). Cavern systems can also provide preferential flowpaths for water and contaminants, knowledge of which may be important in water resource investigations or hazardous waste characterization. Noninvasive techniques helpful in locating cavities include certain geophysical techniques (e.g., microgravity) and fracture-trace analysis using aerial photographs.

Cavities in the subsurface can be either natural, such as caves in karst areas, or human-made, such as tunnels or shafts in mines. Detecting cavities in the subsurface involves locating a region with properties close to those of air or water surrounded by a region with properties of the background geology. Cavities can produce contrasts in a number of physical properties including gravity (see Figure 2.3), dielectric constant, seismic velocity, and electrical conductivity. In addition, cavities may contain increased biological activity due to steep geochemical gradients and interfaces within the cavity. As a result, there may be biogeochemical indicators of the presence of the cavity, such as gases, microbial mats, or bionic mineral accumulations, that can be detected remotely. As in the detection of other objects, the problem of resolution must be considered for any method that is used. The cavities of interest usually range in size from centimeters to tens of meters.

Microgravity surveys are also useful in detecting cavities (Butler, 1984; Hinze, 1994). The contrast in P-wave velocity between the water or air in the cavity and the background geology makes cavities targets for seismic reflection and diffraction methods as well (Steeples and Miller, 1987; Branham and Steeples, 1988). There can be a distinct GPR response associated with the presence of cavities (e.g., Gourry et al., 1995). The dielectric constant of a void filled with air or water will be significantly different from that of the surrounding material.

REFERENCES

Amy, P. S., and D. L. Haldeman, eds., 1997. *Microbiology of the Terrestrial Deep Subsurface*, CRC Press, Boca Raton, Florida.

Benson, R.C., 1991. Remote sensing and geophysical methods for evaluation of subsurface conditions, in *Practical Handbook of Ground-Water Monitoring*, D. M. Nielsen, ed., Lewis Publishers, Chelsea, Michigan, pp. 143-194.

Benson, R. C., R. A. Glaccum, and M. R. Noel, 1982. *Geophysical Techniques for Sensing Buried Waste and Waste Migration*, National Water Well Association, 236 pp.

Benson, J. L., J. M. Jones, V. L. Shelby, and T. C. Kind, 1997. Remotely sensed data/geographic information systems for site evaluation, in *Proceedings of the Symposium on the Application of Geophysics to Engineering and Environmental Problems*, Environmental and Engineering Geophysical Society, 113-116.

Bradford, J., M. Ramaswamy, and C. Peddy, 1996. Imaging PVC gas pipes using 3-D GPR, in *Proceedings of the Symposium on the Application of Geophysics to Engineering and Environmental Problems*, Environmental and Engineering Geophysical Society, 519-524.

Branham, K. L., and D. W. Steeples, 1988. Cavity detection using high-resolution seismic reflection methods, *Mining Engineering 40*, 115-119.

Butler, D. K., 1984. Microgravimetric and gravity gradient surveys for detection of subsurface cavities, *Geophysics 49*(7), 1084-1096.

Chleborad, A. F., S. F. Diehl, and S. H. Cannon, 1996. Geotechnical properties of selected materials from the Slumgullion landslide (Chapter 11), in *The Slumgullion Flow: A Large-Scale Natural Laboratory*, D. J. Varnes and W. Z. Savage, eds., U.S. Geological Survey Bulletin 2130, U.S. Government Printing Office, Washington, D.C.

Cohen, R. M., and J. W. Mercer, 1993. *DNAPL Site Evaluation*, C. K. Smoley, Boca Raton, Florida.

Cohn, M. E., and A. J. Rudman, 1995. Orientation of near-surface fractures from azimuthal measurements of apparent resistivity, *65th Annual Meeting, Society of Exploration Geophysicists*, Expanded Abstracts, 372-374.

Danbom, S. H., 1995. Environmental Geophysics, Society of Exploration Geophysicists Continuing Education Course Notes.

Davis, J. L., and A. P. Annan, 1989. Ground-penetrating radar for high-resolution mapping of soil and rock stratigraphy, *Geophysical Prospecting 37*(5), 531-552.

EPA, 1992. Dense Nonaqueous Phase Liquid—A Workshop Summary, April 16-19, 1991, Dallas Texas, U.S. Environmental Protection Agency report EPA/600/R-92/030, 81 pp.

Fitterman, D. V., and M. Deszcz-Pan, 1998. Helicopter EM mapping of saltwater intrusion in Everglades National park, Florida, *Exploration Geophysics 29*.

Franklin, A. G., D. M. Patrick, D. K. Butler, W. E. Strohm, and M. E. Hynes-Griffin, 1981. Foundation Considerations in Siting of Nuclear Facilities in Karst Terrains and Other Areas Susceptible to Ground Collapse, NUREG/CR-2062, U.S. Nuclear Regulatory Commission, Washington, D.C.

Fredrickson, J. K., and T. C. Onstott, 1996. Microbes deep inside the earth, *Scientific American 275*(4), 68-73.

Ghiorse, W. C.,1997. Subterranean life, *Science 275*, 789-790.

Ghiorse, W. C., and J. T. Wilson, 1988. Microbial ecology of the terrestrial subsurface, *Adv. Appl. Microbiol. 33*, 107-172.

Gourry, J. C., C. Sirieix, L. Bertrand, and F. Mathieu, 1995. 3D diagnosis of a tunnel through infrared thermography combined with ground penetrating radar, in *Proceedings of the Symposium on the Application of Geophysics to Engineering and Environmental Problems*, Environmental and Engineering Geophysical Society, 139-148.

Greenhouse, J., M. Brewster, G. Schneider, D. Redman, P. Annan, G. Olhoeft, J. Lucius, K. Sander, and A. Mazzella, 1993. Geophysics and solvents: The Borden experiment, *The Leading Edge 12*, 261-267.

Hinze, W., 1994. Engineering and environmental applications of gravity and magnetic methods, in *Introduction to Applied Geophysics: Short Course*, Environmental and Engineering Geophysical Society.

Hoekstra, P., and B. Hoekstra, 1991. Geophysics applied to environmental, engineering, and ground water investigations, short course notes, Blackhawk Geosciences, Inc., Bowie, Maryland.

Holloway, A. L., K. M. Stevens, and G. S. Lodha, 1992. The results of surface and borehole radar profiling from permit area B of the Whiteshell research area, Manitoba, Canada, in *Special Paper 16, Geological Survey of Finland*, pp. 329-337.

Killham, K. 1994. *Soil Ecology*, Cambridge University Press, New York.

Lines, L. R., A. K. Schultz, and S. Treitel, 1988. Cooperative inversion of geophysical data, *Geophysics 53*(1), 8-22.

Madsen, E. L., and W. C. Ghiorse. 1993. Ground water microbiology: Subsurface ecosystem processes, in *Aquatic Microbiology: An Ecological Approach*, T. Ford, ed., Blackwell Scientific Publications, Cambridge, Massachusetts, pp. 167-213.

National Research Council (NRC), 1984. *Groundwater Contamination*, National Academy Press, Washington, D.C.

NRC, 1996. *Rock Fractures and Fluid Flow: Contemporary Understanding and Applications*, National Academy Press, Washington, D.C.

Sander, K. A., G. R. Olhoeft, and J. E. Lucius, 1992. Surface and borehole radar monitoring of a DNAPL spill in 3D versus frequency, look angle and time, in *Proceedings of the Symposium on the Application of Geophysics to Engineering and Environmental Problems*, April 26-29, 1992, R. S. Bell, ed., Oakbrook, Illinois, pp. 455-469.

Steeples, D. W., and R. D. Miller, R. D., 1987. Direct detection of shallow subsurface voids using high resolution seismic-reflection techniques, in B. F. Beck and W. L. Wilson, eds., *Karst Hydrogeology: Engineering and Environmental Applications*, A. A. Balkema, Rotterdam, Netherlands, pp. 179-183.

Terzaghi, K., 1929. Effects of minor geologic details on the safety of dams, *American Institute of Mining and Materials Engineering, Technical Publication 215*, pp. 31-44.

U. S. Army Environmental Center (USAEC), 1994. Unexploded ordnance advanced technology demonstration program at Jefferson Proving Ground (Phase I), Report No. SFIM-AEC-ET-CR-94120, U.S. Army Environmental Center, Aberdeen Proving Ground, Maryland.

4

Methods of Characterization

The principal methods for determining subsurface properties are reviewed in this chapter. The methods are reviewed briefly (scientific and technical details can be found in the referenced literature), followed by their range of application and limitations, and the prospects for their improvement. The major noninvasive characterization tools involve geophysical sensing of potential and propagating fields. In addition, a limited number of noninvasive geochemical and geobiological measurements can be made.

Measurements for characterizing the subsurface may be performed from laboratory to planetary scales; from instrument platforms in boreholes, on the surface, and in vehicles (trucks, boats and airplanes); and from satellites in orbit. Some methods work only from certain platforms (e.g., seismic measurements cannot be made from satellites or aircraft), and a few can be done from all (e.g., electromagnetic observations). In general, the closer the instrument is to the material being measured, the higher is the resolution. Measurement techniques "at a distance" (usually from aircraft or satellites) are remote-sensing methods with meter to tens of meter resolution. Measurement techniques requiring boreholes (single-hole well logging; geophysical sensing from hole to hole, hole to surface, surface to hole, hole to tunnel, etc.) are invasive, requiring the drilling of a hole. However, they can often provide greatly improved resolution compared to surface measurements. Many of these invasive well-logging techniques are thoroughly reviewed by Ellis (1987). In noninvasive characterization, the depth of investigation is highly dependent on technique, logistical constraints, and other factors discussed below, ranging from no surface penetration (surface photoimaging) to hundreds of kilometers in depth (seismic and electromagnetic induction).

Independent of sensor type, all of these methods of characterization also can produce anomaly maps. Such maps yield information about the location of places or regions that are somehow different (or anomalous) from other places. Even if only anomaly information is available, it at least guides later invasive investigation (drilling) to sample these differences.

To go beyond simple anomaly maps requires knowledge of the sensor function, logistics of deployment, sensor location and orientation, sources of noise and interference, and so forth. Such information allows computer processing to correct for biases introduced in the measurement process, for example, because of limitations of the instrument (the instrument transfer function), logistical constraints, or sources of noise. Further, such detailed information can allow the modeling of the measurements and prediction of success in problem application as well as interpretation of derived quantities. For example, if fluid flow is of interest, because the techniques only directly measure changes in some physical field (such as electric or elastic fields), the fluid flow parameters have to be derived through modeling.

In all of the methods of characterization, there are certain common problems. Historically, the single largest error often has been precise knowledge of the location and orientation of the measurement sensor. It does not help to have a good measurement but be unable to relocate the measurement site to guide a drill rig to penetrate a contaminant plume. This location sensitivity is especially true of moving sensors in vehicles and satellites, but also of fixed sensors (such as seismic geophones) where later processing and modeling brings out features in the data that must be located. Inadequate locational information has been rumored to be the reason for the failure of more than one site characterization or exploration survey. Adequate location surveying may also take longer and cost more than the geophysical survey, although the growing use of GPS (Global Positioning System) technology is ameliorating this problem.

Another common problem is lack of property contrast. In comparison to lack of optical contrast, which makes it difficult to find a black cat in a dark coal bin, it is easy to find a furry cat against hard coal by touch. Thus, it is important to consider the available contrast in properties between the target and the host background materials.

In a practical sense, many environmental and many engineering geophysical surveys are conducted under less than ideal conditions; for example, often a site is disturbed by human activities including prior excavation of soil or delivery of fill material. Other problems include the presence of either buried or surface utilities such as tunnels, gas lines, sewer drains, and water mains. The mere presence of these more or less passive anthropogenic features disturbs the signals that would otherwise be obtained.

Other noise sources include active field disturbances caused by human activities such as interferences (electromagnetic methods pick up all nearby good conductors, e.g., metallic pipes, wires, and fences), and sources of noise (seismic noise from wind or nearby traffic; electromagnetic noise from radio stations, cellular phones, and so forth). Seismometers can be susceptible to 60 Hz noise from power lines, as well as higher modes of 60 Hz (such as 120 Hz, 240 Hz, etc.). In addition to noise problems, there are often logistical constraints (e.g., denial of access to secure or hazardous areas) and physical requirements (e.g., seismic methods require ground contact and are not often effective through concrete) that are difficult to meet. Each of these is discussed in further detail for the individual method.

There are two major types of geophysical measurements. One is measurement of potential fields that result from forces decaying away from a source of stored energy. The most common potential-field techniques measure gravitational and magnetic fields; less commonly used are thermal and stress fields, which exhibit a quasi-static, nearly time-invariant (or slowly varying) dependence on a force generated by a gradient in a field. For all of these methods, the depth of investigation and the resolution are controlled by the measurement sampling interval. Closely spaced measurements give higher resolution for nearby changes in properties, but the resolution decays exponentially with increasing depth. In general, a discrete object with a high contrast against its background is detectable at a depth ten times the size of the object. Measurements of small perturbations in the large source field are made with part-per-million precision and accuracy.

The other major type of geophysical measurements, uses propagating fields. Propagating fields result from a disturbance in a field within a material medium that has the capability to store energy. Principal techniques include various adaptations of seismology and ground penetrating radar (GPR). Resolution is controlled by the frequency and the velocity of the propagating wave and is generally comparable to a wavelength. Resolution is also related to the geometry of the sensors and may be much better than one wavelength for arrays of sensors. The depth of penetration is linear with the inverse of frequency (period) and controlled by the losses that cause the eventual decay of the propagating wave. Measurements are made of scattered waves in the absence of the source field.

POTENTIAL-FIELD METHODS

Gravity Measurements

Gravity (a potential field) methods measure changes in the earth's natural gravitational field caused by internal variations in bulk density. Density is a basic property of all materials describing the volumetric packing of mass in space. Gravity describes not only the density of minerals but also the packaging of minerals, including fluids and voids in the interparticle spaces (porosity) between mineral grains. The gravity field is a vector quantity pointed toward the center of the earth, with a minor horizontal component near extremes of topography (mountains and canyons). Commercially available sensors are quite simple in principle—measuring the vertical field strength, but they are delicate, expensive, and sophisticated in practice owing to the required precision of measurement (parts per billion) and necessary corrections for location on the earth (altitude and latitude) and for environment (temperature, barometric pressure, tides). Fundamental principles are described in Blakely (1996) and Hinze (1994).

The subsurface condition that leads to a surface anomaly in the gravitational field is a density variation that changes with horizontal location (lateral density contrast) or depth. A variety of geological conditions cause lateral density contrasts (e.g., lithologic changes, cavities, faults, folds) as do buried human-made features (e.g., trenches, tunnels, disposal containers). For example, Roberts et al. (1990a) detected density differences within landfill material in a glaciated area in the U.S. midcontinent.

Applications and Limitations

Applications of gravity address engineering, environmental, groundwater, and archaeological requirements, such as detection of cavities and tunnels, mapping of density variations in landfills or aquifer materials, location of underground storage tanks, location of buried river channels, detection of faults and fracture zones, and infrastructure assessments. Butler (1984) discusses the use of gravity gradients for near-surface investigations. Because gravity measurements can be taken virtually anywhere, surveys are possible on, inside, and immediately adjacent to structures; on pavement and concrete slabs; and under conditions where other noninvasive methods are not always applicable (Yule et al., 1998). However, certain frequencies of mechanical vibrations can make attaining precision measurements difficult.

Future Prospects

Because most technical and theoretical aspects of gravity measurements are quite mature, future improvements will probably be evolutionary in nature. New possibilities are starting to be realized by the application of airborne gravity surveys, which combine gravity determinations with accurate land and sensor positioning using the GPS in a differential mode (NRC, 1994). At present, the resolution of airborne gravity systems are on the order of a few milligals (1 gal = 1 cm/s^2), which is about a thousand times less accurate than microgravity surveys on land. However, the resolution will probably improve with increased attention to this relatively new approach, particularly since it can cover large areas at a smaller cost than land surveys. For certain types of applications, gravity measurements from satellites will be possible (NRC, 1997).

A Department of Defense program in the 1980s helped develop a viable gravity gradiometer system (Jakeli, 1993). The system allows determination of all independent components of the gradient tensor from moving platforms. Diverse applications of the gravity gradiometer measurements are a rapidly evolving area of research (Bell, 1997).

Magnetic Measurements

Magnetic methods measure changes in the earth's natural magnetic (potential) field caused by variations in magnetic susceptibility and remanence. Magnetic susceptibility is the property of some minerals (mostly iron bearing) that describes their ability to be magnetized by an external magnetic field. Magnetic remanence is the property that describes the ability of a material to retain magnetic field strength and direction in the absence of an external magnetic field. Magnetic fields are static vector fields with three-dimensional variation in direction over the surface of the earth with a small superimposed time-varying component. It is sometimes important to measure both field strength and direction. Modern commercial sensors are simple in principle, measuring either the total field strength (a scalar) or the three-components of the directional field (a vector). Gradient measurements (derivatives of the field) are less often measured. Measurements are performed easily and routinely at the part-per-million level. The techniques are quite mature. Fundamental principles are described in Blakely (1996) and Hinze (1994).

Magnetic interpretation is similar to gravity interpretation because both are based on potential-field theory, except that magnetic anomalies are almost always asymmetrical. It is important to realize that anomalies express the net effect of two bipolar vector magnetic fields (induced and remanent) that usually have different intensities and directions of magnetization. Wavelength filtering can be used to better separate the effects of shallow versus deep-seated sources. Using a high-pass filter brings out anomalies at greater depths. Derivative methods accentuate the boundaries of anomalies, both shallow and deep.

As with all potential-field techniques, it is impossible to calculate the anomaly's depth unambiguously without knowing the shape and magnetic properties of the source of a magnetic anomaly. However, with a prior knowledge about the source, it is often possible to estimate depths to within a factor of 10 to 20 percent depending on the complexity of the anomaly and site noise conditions.

Magnetic gradiometry involves simultaneous measurement by two magnetometers close to each other (about 0.5 m). The interval gradient is the difference in magnetic intensity readings divided by the distance between sensors. Commonly, two total field instruments are placed on a vertical staff and the vertical gradient is determined. Two key advantages of gradient surveys are (1) they tend to resolve complex anomalies into their component parts (higher resolution than the magnetic field alone), and (2) because the readings are taken simultaneously, it is not necessary to correct for diurnal variations and magnetic storms. The orientation of the line between the two sensors must be kept constant, or at least monitored, because the gradient will vary with the orientation of this line. In addition, the magnetic cleanliness of the operator (belt buckles, watches, etc.) and magnetic cleanliness of the surface of the area surveyed become even more important than for simple total field measurements. The gradiometer technique is extremely sensitive to surface debris such as nails, cans, wire, and other metallic objects.

Applications, Limitations, and Prospects

In site characterization, magnetic methods commonly are used for finding buried objects such as drums and abandoned underground fuel storage tanks. Often, the analysis can be very simple. A survey is carried out on a grid or profile line, the results are contoured or plotted, and anomaly locations are noted. Buried metallic objects usually show up as dipolar anomalies (magnetic highs with an adjacent low on their north sides in the Northern Hemisphere). However, sophisticated filtering and analysis techniques for separation of superimposed anomalies and depth determinations can make processing and interpreting magnetic surveys more complicated (e.g., Telford et al., 1990; Burger, 1992).

Where there are localized changes or contrasts in magnetic properties, the earth's field will induce a secondary or anomalous magnetic field. For buried ferrous metal objects, the magnetic permeability is large relative to surrounding soil and rock and results in a large induced magnetic field. Many magnetic objects, particularly ferromagnetic objects, also have a large remanent or permanent component. Accurate interpretation of magnetic data depends on being able to distinguish between the induced and remanent components.

Gravity and magnetic methods can be used in a complementary fashion to more tightly constrain geological interpretations. Roberts et al. (1990b) give an example in which magnetic data recorded over a landfill was enhanced by digital processing. Hinze et al. (1990) show how the gravity and magnetic data from the landfill can be combined to assist in the interpretation of its extent and of the material within it.

Future prospects include several innovations related to increased use of GPS, high-temperature superconductivity, and cheaper electronics. Increased use of GPS could lead to robotic control of magnetometers, including unmanned aircraft. High-temperature superconductors may lead to additional sensitivity for portable magnetometers. Cheaper electronics and computing could lead to real-time contouring of data in the field and to increased use of magnetic gradiometry in which two or more magnetometers are read simultaneously at slightly different locations.

ELECTRICAL AND ELECTROMAGNETIC METHODS

"Electrical methods" refer to measurements of natural or impressed electrical fields (potential fields) at low-frequency alternating current (ac) or direct

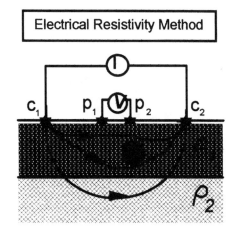

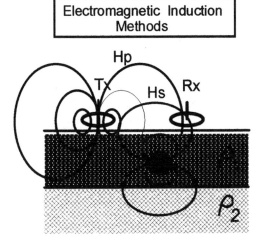

FIGURE 4.1   Simple comparison of electrical resistivity methods and electromagnetic induction (EM) methods. EM methods are generally noncontact, whereas resistivity methods require driving metal electrodes into the ground.

current (dc) using electrodes attached to the ground. By contrast, electromagnetic (EM) methods measure magnetic fields associated with time-varying subsurface currents induced by a natural or artificial electromagnetic source (propagating fields). A schematic comparison of the two is shown in Figure 4.1. GPR is based on high-frequency electromagnetic wave propagation.

Field Electrical Measurements

Electrical field methods measure changes in the earth's natural and induced electrical fields caused by changes in the source origins of the fields and in the electrical properties of the earth. Electrical field methods include dc resistivity, complex resistivity, and self potential. Electrical properties of interest are (1) the electrical conductivity, which describes the ability of a material to transport electrical charge, and (2) certain electrochemical and coupled processes. Sources of the electrical fields are the natural fields in the earth caused by the natural magnetic field, solar-wind interaction with the earth, lightning from storms, electrochemistry (e.g., the battery-like corrosion of naturally occurring sulfide minerals in water), and coupled processes (e.g., a voltage called the streaming potential is generated by fluids flowing through pores). Human-made sources also exist from grounding of power grids, corrosion of buried metallic objects, and intentional artificial sources connected to the ground (dc resistivity sounding).

Electrical fields are time-varying vector fields with three-dimensional variation in direction over the surface of the earth. Commercial electric field sensors are simple in principle, consisting of a porous container filled with nonpolarizing electrolyte and electrode. Measurements are made by connecting voltmeter terminals to electrodes in the ground at two locations. Measurements are easily and routinely performed at the microvolt or millivolt level. Fundamental principles are described in Keller and Frischknecht (1970), for example.

dc Resistivity

The dc resistivity method is a widely used, inexpensive technique for near-surface investigations. Electrical resistivity methods measure the bulk electrical resistivity of the subsurface directly by measuring the voltage generated by transmission of current between electrodes implanted at the ground surface (Figure 4.2). Resistivity data are collected using single or multiple pairs of current and voltage electrodes (dipoles) with known relative positions. They are interpreted by matching them to theoretical models having a subsurface structure of varying conductivity.

In the past, resistivity measurements were usually taken in a straight line on the surface, and the interpretation was done in terms of one-dimensional or two-dimensional models. In a sounding, the measurement array can be expanded about a central position and the data interpreted with a vertical one-dimensional model. In profiling, the relative array geometry and electrode spacing are fixed, but the entire array is moved laterally. Variations indicate lateral or two-dimensional changes in subsurface resistivity. This work can be reviewed in texts such as Keller and Frischknecht (1970) and Koefoed (1979).

Sounding provides a resistivity map as a function of depth, comparable to drilling a well and logging it for this information. Resistivity measurements are

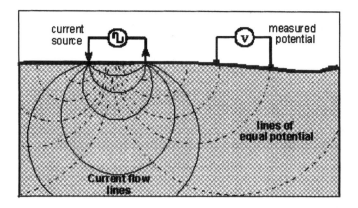

FIGURE 4.2   Schematic of a resistivity survey.

made at a variety of electrode separations, the depth of the investigation increasing with larger separations. Electrode geometry can differ among various applications of this method. Profiling is performed using a constant spacing between electrodes (two outside current electrodes and two inside voltage probes), in which case the arrangement is known as a Wenner configuration (Figure 4.2), and sounding using the Schlumberger configuration where the potential electrodes are located in the center of two widely spaced current electrodes. Modern resistivity systems use a multicore cable, multiple electrodes, and computer-controlled switches in a noise-reducing and field-efficient procedure that speeds the data collection process. Depth and resistivity estimates are made with one- or two-dimensional inversion programs.

Complex resistivity or induced polarization measurements refer to nonlinear or frequency-dependent resistivity measurements and are treated later in this chapter.

It was clear even from early studies (Schlichter, 1933; Pekeris, 1940) that results of the resistivity method must account carefully for both nonuniqueness and resolution issues. More recently, there have been systematic studies of the uniqueness of one-dimensional resistivity sounding results (Parker, 1984; Zohdy, 1989; Simms and Morgan, 1992). A number of easy-to-use one-dimensional inversion programs are commercially available.

Recently, a number of approximate imaging schemes have been developed (e.g., Niwas and Israil, 1987; Zohdy, 1989) that give a better representation of a spatially varying geoelectric section than simple layered-earth models.

Two-dimensional resistivity models of the subsurface avoid some of the limitations in one-dimensional models. Clearly, they also entail the collection of much more data. The first step in data processing is usually to display the data graphically in a pseudosection, which is constructed by assigning a resistivity value, measured with a specific geometry, to an approximate position at depth. The pseudosection is a data display, not a geoelectric section. Unfortunately, some practitioners mistakenly contour this pseudosection and use it as the end product for interpretation. Resistivity data may be inverted on a computer using algorithms (e.g., Tripp et al., 1984).

Today, the state of the science is to collect extensive current and electrical potential data not in one direction but rather in two surface directions. These data are then interpreted by computer inversion in terms of two-dimensional or three-dimensional subsurface models. Hundreds to thousands of data points must be collected. The generation and inversion of a full three-dimensional subsurface model requires complex computer codes (Ellis and Oldenburg, 1994; Li and Oldenburg, 1994; Zhang et al., 1995). However, the general uniqueness and resolution of three-dimensional resistivity inversion have not been investigated sufficiently thus far.

Self Potential

Self potentials (SP) (sometimes called spontaneous potential) are natural dc voltages that exist in the earth. They are measured with a high-input impedance voltmeter using nonpolarizing electrodes, often as a by-product of a dc resistivity measurement. Natural voltages rarely exceed 100 mV over several hundred meters, and they usually average to zero over distances that are a few times larger than whatever size anomalies may be present. These electrical fields are caused by fluid flow, subsurface chemical reactions, and temperature differences. Depth of placement of the electrodes can have an effect on the reliability of the readings, as can roots and nearby vegetation.

Through the fluid flow streaming-potential mechanism, the SP method represents the only known noninvasive passive method directly related to subsurface fluid flow (the seismoelectric method also can measure fluid flow). Small fluid flows associated with cracks in contaminant containment barriers are probably too small to be observed. However, significant fluid movement associated with remediation, such as pump-and-treat and sparging, should produce measurable anomalies. Furthermore, significant fluid flow from leaking dams can be monitored and modeled (e.g., Wurmstich et al., 1991; Wurmstich and Morgan, 1994).

Underground chemical pollution, by definition, produces chemical concentration or diffusion potentials. However, a number of factors must be favorable for surface anomalies to be detectable. Large chemical concentration differences, shallow depth, and a high electrical resistivity background all contribute to enhancing the effect. Furthermore, the specific chemistry involved in setting up the diffusion potentials will determine the level of sustainable electric current available from such an electrochemical battery.

The SP method is one of the oldest geophysical methods and shows significant correlation with subsurface processes. Field data are also relatively easy and inexpensive to obtain. However, detailed interpretation is relatively difficult. Because the voltages are low, they are subject to noise from power lines, pipelines, electrical storms, and other environmental sources. Care must be taken with the data acquisition field procedures to ensure that the data are repeatable.

Induced Polarization (IP)

Using an electrode setup identical to that of the resistivity method, the response of the ground to the removal of an induced electrical signal can be investigated. The IP method involves measurement of the decay of voltage in the ground following the cessation of an excitation current pulse (time-domain method) or low-frequency (less than 100 Hz) variations of earth impedance (frequency-domain method). Most of the stored energy involved is chemical, involving variations in the mobility of ions and variations due to the change from ionic to electronic conduction where metallic minerals are present, and can be likened to a capacitive discharge. Various electrode configurations can be used, commonly dipole-dipole arrays.

In the resistivity method, the passage of electric current through the pores of rocks and soils is dominated by the movement of ions in the pore solution. The earth behaves capacitively at low frequency. Induced polarization measures the low-frequency or capacitive behavior. As ions progress through the pore fluid of rocks they also accumulate along and across surface boundaries. It is this induced accumulation of charge that produces the capacitive effect.

Induced polarization is present in varying degrees in all earth materials. However, it manifests itself strongly in two situations. When electrically conducting metallic minerals are present, charges accumulate at surface boundaries as charge flow changes from ionic in solution to electronic through the mineral. IP effects are also significant in earth materials such as clays with high internal surface areas. Here the charge accumulation or capacitance is associated with the ubiquitous electrochemical boundary layer.

Application, Limitations, and Improvement of IP Methods

Traditionally, IP was assessed in the field by measuring the resistivity at two frequencies or by monitoring the change in decay in response to a current pulse. Modern instruments can also measure the phase difference between the real and imaginary parts (complex conductivity) over a wide range of frequency. Such instrumentation opens a new domain because it allows a broad frequency or spectral response to be recorded in the field. The idea is that the spectral response will have behaviors characteristic of the specific chemical reactions taking place.

Historically, IP has been used mainly to locate metallic minerals in the near surface (Wait, 1959; Madden and Cantwell, 1967; Bertin and Loeb, 1976; Sumner, 1976). There were a few early attempts to use the method in groundwater studies (Vacquier et al., 1957). Currently, with the widespread emphasis on environmental problems, there has been renewed interest in IP. The idea is that pollutants may alter or influence the surface chemistry and attendant chemical reactions in such a manner that the IP response will be anomalous relative to unpolluted areas. How successful this will be is still a matter of debate, but IP represents one of the few means of possibly performing noninvasive chemistry. As a parallel to the above, because IP is sensitive to clays at depth, it is often of tremendous use in mapping low-permeability clay zones that impede pollutant movement. The negative side of this sensitivity is that it is not possible to uniquely determine if an IP anomaly is due to the actual contamination or to the confining clay zone.

The current status of practice is to perform single-frequency, time-domain or phase IP and to plot this as a pseudosection at an approximate depth. Layered-earth IP inversion is the current state of the art, but is not widely practiced. In addition, techniques for two-dimensional IP inversion have also been developed (e.g., Pelton et al., 1978), and attempts are being made to perform three-dimensional IP inversion (Oldenburg and Li, 1994). The main limitations appear to be lack of consistent high-quality, high-volume data and dissemination of computer codes.

The IP method has some unique features and possibilities in terms of non-invasive chemical characterization. Good instrumentation is available for embarking on the more interesting spectral IP and three-dimensional interpretation methods, and the subject is moving mainly in this direction. Recommendations for needed research in IP are given by Ward et al. (1995), and condensed below:

• Opportunities exist in the areas of controlled laboratory and in situ measurement to better understand IP signatures of various chemical contaminant situations, especially rock-fluid interactions at a wide range of frequencies.
• Further development of digital signal processing and both forward and inverse modeling techniques for IP methods could enhance the extraction of relevant geophysical parameters from IP data.
• For environmental work, research in IP data acquisition using the order of 100 data recording channels is needed, along with systems that would quickly, efficiently, and safely control a large array of electrodes with minimal human intervention.

Low-Frequency Electromagnetic Field Measurements

Electromagnetic induction techniques operate at frequencies less than 1 MHz and are based on inducing eddy currents at the surface. Eddy currents diffuse into the earth at a rate that depends on the electrical conductivity and, to lesser extent, the magnetic susceptibility of the earth. At induction frequencies, the attenuation of electromagnetic waves is proportional to the square root of conductivity and frequency.

At high frequencies (generally greater than 1 MHz), electromagnetic fields propagate like seismic waves, responding mostly to the complex dielectric permittivity and, to a lesser extent, to the electrical conductivity and complex magnetic susceptibility. Electromagnetic measurements above 1 MHz are generally referred to as GPR, which is discussed later in this chapter. Electromagnetic waves are three-dimensional, time-varying, complex vector fields, propagating with directional and polarization properties. Electromagnetic waves may be of natural or induced origin, such as power grids, electric subways, and communications broadcasts.

At lower frequencies, the commercial sensors are coils of wire (magnetic sensors or induction coils), and at high frequencies, the commercial sensors are electric field antennas. Measurements are made of the strength (magnitude and phase) and orientation (direction and polarization) of the complex vector fields.

Frequency-Domain Electromagnetics

This active (as opposed to passive) induction technique uses a transmitting coil that emits a fixed- or swept-frequency EM oscillation and a receiving coil that measures changes in amplitude and phase of the secondary magnetic field associated with eddy currents induced in the ground. These eddy currents and their associated secondary magnetic fields are directly proportional to the electrical properties of the shallow subsurface sediments and fluids beneath and between the two coils. The simplest frequency-domain EM instruments, known as terrain conductivity meters, yield depth-integrated measurements of soil conductivity from a depth of a meter to more than 30 m. Conductivity data can be interpreted qualitatively or quantitatively, often in conjunction with other procedures designed to directly measure conductivity as a function of depth, such as resistivity sounding. The depth of investigation from frequency-domain EM procedures is a function of coil separation, transmitted frequency, and transmitter power. The end product is a map showing conductivity (millisiemens or millimhos per meter) as a function of lateral position and is used for reconnaissance of a site's electrical properties from the surface down to some depth of interest. Results from a high-resolution frequency-domain EM system at the University of Arizona are shown in Plate 2.

Recently, there has been interest in high-frequency EM surveys (Sternberg and Poulton, 1997). At frequencies of 1 to 30 MHz, it is possible to measure both conductivity and dielectric constant. At these frequencies, the depth of penetration of the EM energy is much greater in conductive soils, compared with standard GPR, which typically uses frequencies of 30 MHz to 1 GHz. The measurement of both conductivity and dielectric constant provides greatly enhanced capability to infer more about the earth's properties (e.g., presence of organic contaminants, engineered structures, and buried nonmetallic objects).

Time-Domain Electromagnetics

Time-domain EM techniques are fundamentally similar to frequency-domain EM methods, except the transmitted signal is in the form of discrete pulses and the secondary magnetic field is measured during the interval between pulses. The rate of decay of the secondary magnetic field depends on the electrical conductivity structure in the earth. In the presence of highly conductive bodies, the decay is slower than in a less conductive earth. The decay signal can be interpreted in terms of lateral and depth variations in conductivity. The depth of investigation increases with sample time and decreases with ground conductivity, but it can penetrate more than 100 m in some cases. For near-surface investigations, very early time systems have been developed with small portable transmitter loops suitable for rapid profiling. An application of time-domain EM is illustrated in Plate 3.

Very Low Frequency Electromagnetics

This technique measures the magnetic (and sometimes electric) components of the electromagnetic field generated by long-distance radio transmitters in the very low frequency (VLF) band. These transmitters are used for long-distance naval communication with submarines and operate in the 10- to -30-kHz frequency range. Conductive structures on the surface or underground, even when covered with thick overburden, locally affect the direction and strength of the field generated by the transmitted radio signal. The method can locate structures where quantities of groundwater may be held in rock fractures or cavities, and it is sensitive to geological features with long strike length. Large anomalies are associated with electrical cables and buried metallic pipes in urban areas. Commercial adaptations display the in-phase and quadrature magnetic field tilt-angle components from which interpretations of lateral changes in conductivity are made. If topsoil is electrically conductive, it is difficult to obtain information from deeper structures. Some VLF equipment also measures the electric field, allowing calculation of average ground conductivity.

Applicability of Electrical and Electromagnetic Methods

Electrical and electromagnetic methods have tremendous potential for significant advancements in the field of near-surface investigations. They are currently among the most used techniques for environmental and engineering site investigations, however their potential is far greater than is currently being realized. Applications include site stratigraphy, depth to the groundwater table or electrically conductive contaminant plumes, and buried wastes. Time-lapse measurements can help detect leaks in engineered contaminant barriers or in tracking the movement of contaminant plumes.

Electromagnetic methods (in contrast with seismic or GPR) have relatively low resolution. Nevertheless, theoretical studies show that EM techniques can have much higher resolution than is achieved currently in normal field surveys. For example, Fullager (1984) showed that these methods "are, in principle, imbued with unlimited resolving power ... provided no noise is present." A small amount of noise, which is always present to some degree, can have significant degrading effects on the resolving power.

Electromagnetic methods can be particularly sensitive to the parameters of greatest interest in near-surface investigations. These methods include direct detection of contaminants in the subsurface, sensitivity to geological formation changes, and a correlation with parameters of interest in geotechnical studies. Although there have been controlled demonstrations indicating sensitivity of the EM fields to some of these parameters, much more development of this technology is needed to apply this in routine field surveys.

Electromagnetic systems are in many respects relatively crude in comparison, for example, to standard three-dimensional seismic survey systems used in the petroleum industry. Some of the pressure to use simpler and relatively unsophisticated instrumentation comes from the desire to emphasize low cost, easy-to-use, and easy-to-understand techniques. Unfortunately, this has limited the usefulness of the techniques and has resulted in much greater expense during drilling and excavation phases in some site investigations.

Electromagnetic measurements can use an almost endless variety of sources, instruments (e.g., receivers, array types, recording techniques) and techniques (e.g., those discussed above). On the one hand, this is a great advantage because of the wide diversity of measurements and the opportunity for novel techniques. On the other hand, it is also a disadvantage because much of the past effort in this field has been diffused over a great many different, and incompatible, techniques. Controlled tests are needed to help define the best approaches for each problem of interest in near-surface investigations.

Potential Improvements of Electrical and EM Capabilities

There are a great many potential research and technical improvements in capabilities. Among those that can be undertaken are the following:

- More sophisticated arrays of sensors and sources.
- Further development of broadband measurements from dc to gigahertz frequencies.
- More rapid data collection to allow essentially continuous profiling and areal coverage.
- Greatly enhanced capabilities to handle cultural interference, in particular grounding-line interference, not just electrical noise.
- Sophisticated systems for critical applications where the alternative would

be expensive excavation, as well as more economical, easier-to-use systems that contain a subset of new capabilities for EM systems that could be operated in smaller-scale surveys by skilled technicians.

• Interpretations that more often include complex resistivity at low frequencies and combined use of conductivity and dielectric constant at higher frequencies.

• Published case histories are essential for showing applications of improved EM techniques for mapping properties of interest in near-surface investigations, including more studies of contaminant mapping, permeability determination, formation type, rock strength, and water chemistry. There has been a number of case histories studying some of these properties, but, few have used the full capabilities of EM, including novel arrays, wide bandwidths, complex resistivity and dielectric constants, and high data density measurements.

• New field acquisition methods will require greatly improved interpretation techniques that allow handling of complex geometries and widely varying background responses. These techniques include analytical, numerical, and physical modeling as well as novel methods of transforming the raw data into a meaningful image of the subsurface.

• Easy-to-use interpretation techniques that allow some of the interpretation to be done in near real time in the field.

• More laboratory electrical property measurements are needed to determine what can be interpreted reliably from surface electrical and electromagnetic measurements. For example, are there distinctive electrical property changes due to contaminants, what is the relationship between engineering properties such as rock strength and electrical properties, and how well can hydraulic permeability be predicted from electrical properties? Another crucial area for laboratory electrical property studies is to find ways to better relate laboratory-scale measurements to field-scale measurements.

GROUND PENETRATING RADAR

GPR is similar to the seismic reflection method in the basic wave propagation physics, but uses high-frequency electromagnetic waves in the tens of megahertz to gigahertz range. Details of the acquisition process differ markedly from the seismic method, most notably because only one channel is acquired. The contrasts being measured with GPR are differences in dielectric permittivity across earth boundaries. The dielectric permittivity is a measure of the ability of a material to store electrical charge (like a capacitor or battery) and principally determines the velocity of propagation of the electromagnetic wave. The product of the dielectric permittivity and the magnetic permeability is analogous to seismic impedance. The real part of this product (complex modulus) usually describes how the material stores energy and the imaginary part describes how the material loses (or dissipates) energy.

The EM wave propagates in the earth at the speed of light divided by the square root of the dielectric constant of the geological material. The depth of investigation is inversely proportional to the near-surface conductivity of soils and pore fluids. Due to the smaller wavelengths used in the GPR method, resolution is commonly as much as one order of magnitude better than current seismic reflection techniques.

The quality of GPR data and its usefulness in site characterization are determined by (1) the electrical properties of the site, (2) the equipment used, (3) data acquisition procedures and parameters, (4) data processing, and (5) methodologies for interpretation and visualization. The greatest limitation to the widespread use of GPR is the electrical conductivity at a site, which determines the depth of penetration. As a rough guide, GPR is considered to be most useful when the conductivity is less than 10 mS/m (Davis and Annan, 1989); this generally prevents effective applications of GPR in clay-rich environments.

Applications of Ground Penetrating Radar

GPR is used to delineate near-surface site stratigraphy, map the extent of buried waste, locate the water table, and find buried utilities. Recent developments in GPR allow direct detection of organic contaminants by observing changes in scattering properties (the texture of the radar record) or dielectric contrast (e.g., oil floating on water).

GPR can contribute to site characterization in three ways. The most common use of GPR is in obtaining information about the large-scale (meters to tens of meters) geological structure at a site. A second common use is to detect anomalous regions superimposed on the natural geological background; this includes the possible detection of liquid contaminants and the detection of buried objects. The third, and most challenging, potential use of GPR is to obtain information at the meter scale (or less) about the specific physical or chemical properties of the subsurface. The first two applications emphasize the use of GPR as a means of imaging the subsurface; in the third, information about dielectric properties is extracted from GPR data and then related to physical and chemical properties. Each of these is expanded upon below.

Large-Scale Imaging

The first step in site characterization often involves determining the geological setting and locating key geological boundaries. Given a site with suitable electrical conductivity, GPR can obtain excellent images of the subsurface that can be used for this purpose. With detailed horizontal and vertical sampling, it is possible to obtain high-resolution (tens of centimeters to meters) images of the subsurface to average depths of 10 m or more. To extract information about the geological structure, the approach usually taken is to identify within the GPR section reflectors with a distinct geometry or orientation, or packages of reflectors with a characteristic appearance.

There are a number of examples in the literature in which GPR data have been used to reconstruct the geological setting by relating the GPR image to the subsurface stratigraphy and sedimentary facies. In such studies there is always prior knowledge from surface outcrop or wells of the lithologies likely to be present and of the depositional environment. Published examples include the use of GPR images to determine the geometry of Pleistocene gravel deposits (Huggenberger et al., 1994), the orientation of major sedimentary structures, and facies thickness and depths in deltaic environments (Jol and Smith, 1991). An example of the GPR image of a deltaic deposit is shown in Figure 4.3. The distinct appearance of the radar reflections makes it relatively easy to locate some sedimentary units in the subsurface. In addition, GPR data can be used to help target the anisotropy expected in hydraulic properties in this sedimentary package. The structure seen in a radar section contains information about the spatial heterogeneity of the subsurface and provides a basis for mapping the geological units in the subsurface.

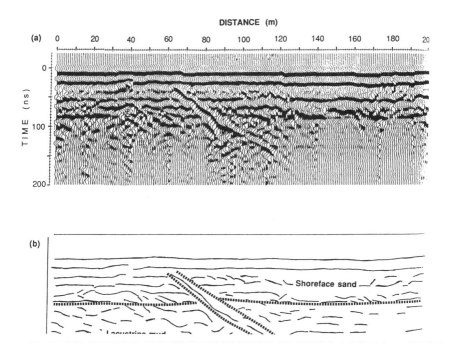

FIGURE 4.3 GPR profile along the escarpment of the Slave River Valley, Fort Smith, North West Territories, Canada. Early Holocene wave-influenced deltaic deposits with possible postdepositional slumping. (From Jol and Smith, 1992.)

70

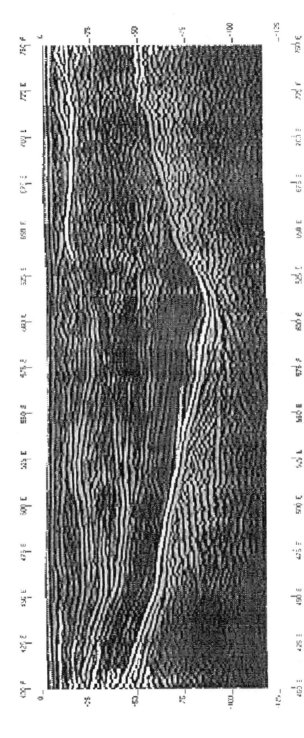

FIGURE 4.4 GPR data presented as a gray-scale shaded section rather than the traditional wiggle trace. The purpose of the survey was to determine the location and shape of a buried river channel.

An important aspect of characterizing the geological setting is to locate the boundaries that can affect the physical, chemical, and biological behavior of regions of the subsurface. One of the key geological boundaries of interest in a number of different applications is the top of the bedrock. This often can be imaged with GPR due to the contrast in dielectric properties between the bedrock and the overlying material. In an example of a GPR image of the bedrock topography under a fine sand overburden (Davis and Annan, 1989), the contrast in dielectric constant between the overlying sand and the granodiorite bedrock and the lateral continuity of the feature made this a relatively easy target for GPR imaging. Further processing of GPR data can improve the presentation of the information (see Figure 4.4).

Determining the depth to the water table is a characterization objective for which GPR is well suited if the electrical conductivity at the site is not high. The water table can be identified as a flat-lying, high-amplitude reflector in a GPR section (Knoll et al., 1991; Sutinen et al., 1992). A dominant reflector is seen due to the contrast between the dielectric constant of the unsaturated and the fully saturated materials; therefore the "water table" reflector seen in GPR sections may actually be the top of the capillary fringe. The clearest images of the top of the saturated zone are obtained in coarse-grained materials where the capillary fringe does not "smear" the dielectric contrast.

Significant progress has been made in the collection and display of GPR data. With current technologies, it is possible to collect and display three-dimensional data in a way that makes it relatively easy for the nonexpert to visualize useful information. This user-friendly aspect of GPR is likely to contribute significantly to the increased use of GPR in site characterization.

In all of the above applications the objective is to obtain a representation of the subsurface in which geological units and boundaries are located. As a useful caveat, the vertical positioning of any feature seen in a GPR record is only as accurate as the velocity determination of the radar signal at that site.

Detection of Organic Contaminants Using GPR

There have been a number of examples in which GPR has been used to image the presence of organic contaminants in the subsurface. The contrast between the low dielectric constant of most organic contaminants and the high dielectric constant of water, and the availability of pre-spill radar data are what make detection possible. A recent example is the direct monitoring of a sinking organic liquid (tetrachloroethylene) during a controlled spill (Annan et al., 1992; Greenhouse et al., 1993; Brewster et al., 1994). This investigation was conducted under the most ideal of conditions: the background geology was a homogeneous sand, and a GPR profile was available from the site before the spill. The collection of GPR data as a function of time during this experiment greatly simplified the interpretation by making it possible to relate the time-dependent changes in the data to the movement of the contaminant. Monitoring such a process is an application for which GPR is well suited.

In a more typical situation, GPR is used after the spill of a contaminant, and time-dependent data are not collected. In some case studies the presence of an organic contaminant has been associated with the region in the GPR record where there is a "washed-out" appearance (Olhoeft, 1986). This change in character of the radar reflectors is by no means a conclusive way of determining the presence—or lack—of a contaminant. This change in GPR signals can lead to a high degree of uncertainty when GPR is used for contaminant detection without additional information from other types of data.

Detection of Buried Objects Using GPR

GPR has been found to be a useful technique for the detection of subsurface voids, buried drums, bodies, storage tanks, and utilities. In some cases, an object can be located using the changes in the dielectric properties in the surrounding zone disturbed during the digging and burial of the object. The main limitations to the use of GPR for these purposes have been the background electrical conductivity of the site, the resolution of the GPR data, and cultural interference.

In many of the GPR searches for buried objects, the procedure is simply to use unprocessed data and look for anomalous regions in terms of the appearance of the GPR reflectors. Looking for anomalous regions is usually what is done in archeological and forensic studies, where there are many examples of the successful use of a GPR image to locate an object in the subsurface. Undoubtedly, there have also been numerous times that regions identified as "anomalous" have not corresponded to the target of interest; unfortunately, it is more difficult to find published examples of these failures. A description of various case studies in which GPR was used both successfully and unsuccessfully to find buried bodies is given by Mellett (1996), with a discussion of the various reasons a GPR anomaly can be associated with the burial.

If digital signal processing capabilities are available, the ability to resolve the presence of a buried object can be improved dramatically. Examples are given in Bradford et al. (1996), where advanced processing methods were used to improve the resolution of GPR data for the purpose of locating metal and polyvinyl chloride (PVC) pipes. Clear images were obtained of pipes with diameters near the limits of resolution (2 inches in this case) for the antennas used in the survey.

Characterizing Small-Scale Properties by GPR

In the above applications, the GPR was used to obtain information about the geological structure of the subsurface or the presence of anomalous fluids or solids. It is the geometry and character of the reflectors in the GPR data that are used in a predominantly qualitative way to characterize the subsurface. It is for imaging the subsurface in this way that GPR is currently most widely used and, given the current technology, most ideally suited for. There is, however, additional information contained in GPR data that can, ideally, be extracted for the purposes of site characterization.

GPR image obtained at a site is one representation of the recorded changes in .dielectric properties of the subsurface. Given that dielectric properties are related to the physical and chemical properties of the subsurface, it should be possible to extract information about these properties from GPR data. Determination of the dielectric properties is not commonly done in practice and represents one of the current limits (or forefronts) in applying GPR to site characterization problems. The two main challenges are in collecting sufficient data to allow inversion for dielectric information and in relating dielectric properties to the physical and chemical properties of interest. A recent example (Greaves et al., 1996) in which GPR data were used to obtain estimates of water saturation at a site illustrates both the problems with and the enormous potential for using GPR data in this way. Currently, GPR can provide excellent images; the future is to provide detailed information about physical, chemical, and biological properties that can be used in characterizing the subsurface.

Opportunities for Improvement of GPR

GPR is a relatively young observational technique. Research needs in GPR, to some degree, resemble those of reflection seismology about 40 years ago. Research is needed in data acquisition, data processing, and inversion and interpretation of the data. Some specific examples in these four areas are given below.

• The use of multichannel receiving antennas would allow much faster recording of data with different distances between source antenna and receiving antennae.

• Multichannel receiving antennae would also allow the use of true three-dimensional recording in an efficient manner.

• New strategies for introducing GPR source energy into the ground, including pulse coding and swept frequency techniques, should improve the penetration depth and image resolution.

• Collection of cross-polarized data would make it possible to characterize the full vector nature of the electromagnetic wave field. This would lead to new ways of discriminating among subsurface targets.

• Digital signal processing of GPR data using reflection seismology data processing software has been on the increase, but algorithm development is needed that accounts for the aspects of GPR data that are not common to seismic methods. For example, processing is required to account for dispersion due to frequency-dependent attenuation and scattering, both of which are much more dominant in GPR data than in seismic data.

• A better understanding of factors that affect the source waveform (e.g., antenna radiation patterns, antenna-ground coupling) would lead to improved deconvolution techniques, which would enhance the temporal resolution. Characterizing the source waveform is also a critical part of developing full waveform inversion techniques.

• Inversion of the GPR data to obtain a dielectric model is a critical step in using GPR data to describe the structure and properties of the subsurface. Inversion methods are needed that account for the complex nature of EM wave propagation.

• An understanding of the link between the dielectric properties of the subsurface, as imaged in GPR data, and material properties (water content, porosity, permeability) is fundamental if we are to use GPR data to describe the magnitude and spatial variation of material properties in the subsurface.

SEISMIC METHODS

Sound waves propagate through air or water as waves (like the ripples around a rock thrown into a pond). In the earth at lower frequencies, such waves are called seismic waves. In fluids (air or water), the mode of propagation is as a pressure wave with particle motion in the direction of wave propagation (called a compressional wave). In solids, there are both compressional waves and shear waves (where particle motion is perpendicular to the direction of propagation, like the motion of a rope laid on the ground and wiggled sideways). At interfaces between two different materials there are a variety of surface wave modes of propagation. The property to which the seismic wave responds is the complex elastic modulus of the material (density dependent), which determines the velocity of propagation and the rate of decay of the propagating signal. The real part of the complex modulus describes how the material stores energy, and the imaginary part describes how the material loses (or dissipates) energy. Seismic waves are three-dimensional, time-varying, complex vector fields, propagating with directional and polarization properties. Seismic waves may be of natural or anthropogenic origin.

Seismic waves are generated naturally by earthquakes (the breaking of rocks under stress), landslides, and events in the ocean and atmosphere (like thunder from lightning). Seismic waves are also generated from anthropogenic sources such as explosions, hammer strikes, and vehicular traffic.

Seismic methods are concerned with the production, propagation, and measurement of elastic waves that travel within earth materials. The variety of seismic sources commonly used for shallow environmental and engineering investigations includes sledgehammers, weight-drop devices, and explosive sources—often in the form of large-gauge shotgun shells fired by percussive or electrical means. Two commonly measured elastic body waves that propagate in the earth are compressional (P) and shear (S) waves. P- and S-waves have veloci-

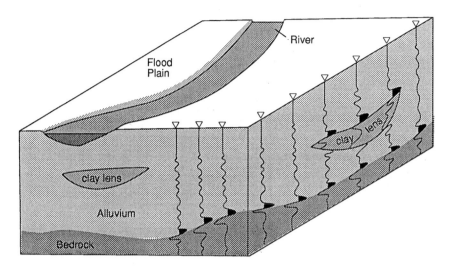

FIGURE 4.5   Simplified cartoon showing the "mapping" of bedrock and other features by seismic waves traced to individual geophone receivers.

ties related to the physical properties of the material in which they travel.[1] The wave velocities are inversely proportional to the square root of density and directly proportional to the square root of the shear modulus for both types of elastic waves and, in addition, bulk modulus for compressional waves.

Detectors (geophones) are implanted in the ground and arrayed at known distances and locations from the controlled energy source (see, for example, Figure 4.5). Precise times of the arrival of the initial seismic waves and subsequent vibrations are recorded at each geophone; also recorded are the amplitude and period of the waves. The receivers are digital, multichannel detectors that respond to particle-velocity changes associated with the passage of the elastic wave. Seismic methods have also been applied in cross-borehole environments, where the geophones are deployed down boreholes to a known depth. In addition to the physical parameters affecting their velocities, seismic waves are reflected, refracted, and variably attenuated (absorbed) as they pass through media with different elastic properties. These properties allow their use in the interpretation

---

[1]The P-wave velocity is $V_p = \sqrt{\left(\dfrac{K + \dfrac{4\mu}{3}}{\rho}\right)}$, and the S-wave velocity is $V_s = \sqrt{\left(\dfrac{\mu}{\rho}\right)}$, where K is the bulk modulus, μ is shear modulus, and ρ is the density of the material.

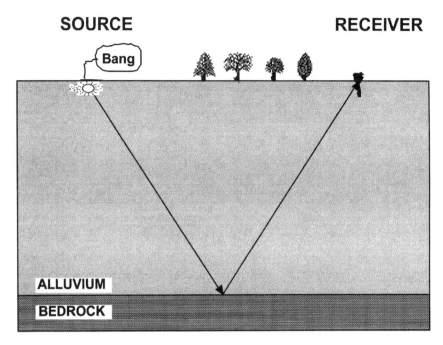

FIGURE 4.6   Simple reflection from bedrock. Either a seismic wave-velocity contrast or a mass density contrast is required for seismic waves to be reflected from the geological interface.

of geological layering and waste-zone geometry based on analysis of signal travel time and frequency content.

The seismic *reflection* method is an image-based technique that produces a cross section of the volume of earth under investigation and shows acoustic-impedance contrasts. The cross section (image of the actual data) has traverse distance as the abscissa and reflected-wave travel time as the ordinate. These acoustic-impedance contrasts can be associated with both fluid and rock boundaries within the earth. The returning signals that constitute the image are stored as traces associated with a particular ground position along the traverse. Each trace is a mathematical vector of particle velocity as a function of time for that position (see Figure 4.6). As these traces are lined up side by side and corrected for geometrical aspects of their acquisition, the individual responses make an echo mosaic that has the appearance of an image of the shallow-earth cross section.

The seismic *refraction* technique uses a series of geophones arrayed on the surface to analyze the refraction of seismic waves along subsurface interfaces of differing materials, as indicated in Figure 4.7. The technique records the time of the first response of each geophone. Plotting these responses as a function of location from the source and processing the information produces a cross section of seismic wave velocity, which reflects geological layering of the subsurface.

Many seismic methods were first developed in the petroleum industry as a way of interpreting the geological structure of sedimentary basins. The signals can be processed by a computer to produce an image—a seismic reflection profile—of the subsurface to depths of several kilometers. An uninterpreted profile is not a true geological cross section, although the gross geometry of the bedrock can be determined from it. Normally seismic methods do not provide any information about the chemical makeup of pore fluids.

Recent developments include the adaptation of reflection seismology for uses as shallow as a few meters and the civil engineering adaptation of spectral analysis of surface waves (SASW) used in determining shear wave velocity profiles and soil stiffness for ground response analyses. The SASW method has a variety of earthquake, environmental, and other geotechnical engineering applications; a recent review is given by Stokoe et al. (1994).

SEISMIC REFRACTION

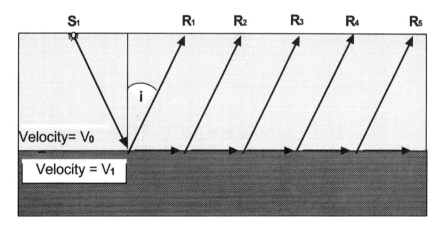

$$\sin i = V_0/V_1$$

FIGURE 4.7   Seismic refraction. Seismic energy produced by source (S) is detected at a series of geophone receivers (R) after traversing the surface layer and refracting along the interface between layers having two different seismic wave velocities. The velocity in the lower layer must be higher than that in the surface layer for the method to work properly.

Applications of Near-Surface Seismology

There are relative advantages and disadvantages of both refraction and reflection seismic techniques (Table 4.1). The reflection technique can be more powerful in terms of generating interpretable observations over complex geological structures. This power, however, comes at a cost, because reflection surveys are more expensive than refraction surveys and more computationally intensive. Also, usable reflections are often not obtained in shallow surveys. As a result, many engineering and environmental concerns generally opt for refraction surveys when possible. On the other hand, the petroleum industry uses reflection seismic methods almost exclusively.

As more channels become available, the increased use of three-dimensional engineering surveys can be expected along with additional applications. The successful use of near-surface seismology spans the spectrum of applications— from those that are well understood and routine to those that are beyond present understanding and technical capabilities. It is important to distinguish where these limits are because vendors and consultants sometimes make unrealistic claims about the capabilities (particularly their capabilities) of near-surface seismic techniques.

Seismic Refraction

Historically, the use of seismic refraction techniques in geoscience and civil engineering investigations has been widespread (Stam, 1962; Redpath, 1973; Mooney, 1977). The method has advanced throughout the past half-century, which parallels the use of portable, multichannel seismographs. Improvements in both acquisition and processing of data have allowed geophysicists to account for layer dip and spatial velocity variations of both the target refractor and the overburden soil velocities. Resolution of the geometry of the target refracting surface has been another source of improvement.

Development of the method reached maturity in 1980 with the publication of the generalized reciprocal method (GRM) of seismic refraction interpretation (Palmer, 1980). Since then, most papers on seismic refraction have described refinements of the GRM technique or explained the method to a larger audience through clarification and example (Lankston and Lankston, 1986; Lankston, 1988).

A developing alternative to GRM analysis is refraction travel time tomography (e.g., Zhang and Toksoz, 1998). Tomography tends to work better than GRM when the near-surface seismic velocity structure is not discrete, continuous, gently dipping homogeneous layers. The method is analogous to medical computerized axial tomography (CAT) scans, except that the measurements are made along the earth's surface rather than around a three-dimensional volume. One

TABLE 4.1   Advantages and Disadvantage of Seismic Refraction and Seismic Reflection Methods.

Refraction Method		Reflection Method	
Advantage	Disadvantage	Advantage	Disadvantage
Observations generally use fewer source and receiver locations; relatively cheap to acquire	Observations require relatively large source-receiver offsets	Observations are collected at small source-receiver offsets	Many source and receiver locations must be used to produce meaningful images; expensive to acquire
Little processing is needed except for trace scaling or filtering to help pick arrival times of the initial ground motion	Only works if the speed at which motions propagate increases with depth	Method can work no matter how the propagation speed varies with depth	Processing can be expensive as it is very computer intensive, needing sophisticated hardware and high-level of expertise.
Modeling and interpretations fairly straightforward	Observations generally interpreted in layers that can have dip and topography; produces simplified models	Reflection observations can be more readily interpreted in terms of complex geology; subsurface directly imaged from observations	Interpretations require more sophistication and knowledge of the reflection process

approach employs a two-point ray tracing technique to calculate forward travel times for a model, followed by a least-squares inversion to fit the data to a model that is iteratively adjusted to reduce the misfit between the data and the modeled traveltimes (White, 1989).

Applications in Which Shallow Refraction Usually Works. A common use of the GRM technique is determining the thickness of the soil column (depth to bedrock) and thereby producing an image of a layer (soil) over a half-space (bedrock). Locating channels in the bedrock surface and the fill material in these channels that differentially control the flow of fluids in the subsurface is another important use of the GRM refraction technique. These channels represent a natural "French drain" that needs to be known and charted in the subsurface in order to install the proper remediation system at the site (Young et al., 1995). If information about the subsurface is obtained on the basis of drill hole information alone, the phenomenon of "spatial aliasing" of these crucial channels could create a distorted view of the subsurface (Henson and Sexton, 1991).

Applications in Which Shallow Refraction Sometimes Works. One current use of GRM seismic refraction is finding zones of increased fracture density within areas of bedrock where flow and transport of groundwater might occur. Several investigators have succeeded in seismically finding fracture zones by noting decreased target refractor velocity along a segment of the bedrock.

Applications in Which Shallow Refraction Does Not Work. One basic theoretical assumption with seismic refraction is that seismic velocity increases with depth. If this assumption is not true at a given site, refraction methods will give incorrect depths or thicknesses of one or more layers. Lankston (1988) discusses ways to detect these errors and to estimate how large such errors might be.

Seismic Reflection

Three conditions must exist for shallow seismic reflection to work. First, the frequency must be high enough for the reflection to be separable from other arrivals in the early part of the seismogram. In general, 3 to 5 cycles of dominant period of the data in time must pass after the onset of the first arrival before the reflection can be easily separated from the direct waves, refractions, and air blast. In some exceptional data sets, this might be reduced to 1.5 to 2 cycles, but investigators who claim such early reflection arrival times must be able to defend such claims with scientific rigor. In a practical sense, for most data sets with dominant frequencies of less than 150 Hz, reflections at times smaller than 50 milliseconds must be demonstrated as valid by the use of phase identification on unstacked data with the phases traceable through the intermediate processing stages.

Second, acoustic impedance contrasts between layers must be large enough to give rise to detectable reflections. These contrasts require a variation in either seismic velocity or material density, or both. Third, the seismic system (energy source, receivers, and seismograph) must work together with sufficient seismic energy and signal sensitivity to register the desired information coming from the ground motion.

Three-dimensional seismic reflection has been widely adopted in the petroleum industry since the mid 1980s. The use of three-dimensional seismic reflection in near-surface work has not been widespread because of the high costs involved. For example, Buker et al. (1998) reported requiring 85 days of field work with a crew of 5 to 7 people to perform a shallow three-dimensional seismic reflection survey of an area 357 m wide by 432 m long.

Applications in Which Shallow Reflection Usually Works. Although one cannot tell in advance of field testing whether shallow seismic reflection will work at a particular site or for a particular objective, it often works in the applications discussed below. Data quality is commonly better where the water table is at a depth of only a few meters and where the near-surface materials have not been

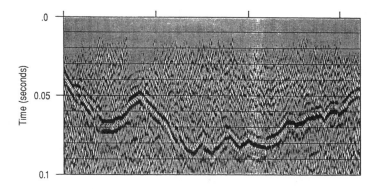

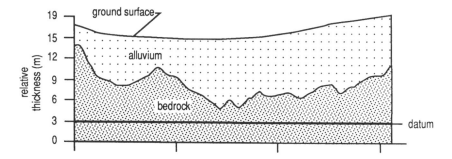

FIGURE 4.8 Seismic reflection cross section and interpreted cross section. The purpose of the characterization was to determine the placement of a monitoring well, which was designed to be placed at the deepest bedrock-alluvium contact. From D. Steeples.

disturbed by construction fill materials or by recent mass wasting such as earthflows or landslides. Working on top of paved surfaces is difficult.

Determining gross geological structure is one of the classic uses of seismic reflection, and the technique works well in near-surface applications if the impedance contrast and frequency are sufficiently large. Examples of this application include determining depth to bedrock (see Figures 4.8 and 4.9) and producing a contour map of bedrock beneath alluvium or till.

Fault detection is another major use of shallow reflection, primarily for earthquake hazard studies, detection of near-surface pathways of high permeability, and geological mapping. Offset detection limits under favorable conditions may be as small as one-tenth of the wavelength of the dominant wave frequency. Because of the reflection time uncertainty introduced by static corrections (e.g.,

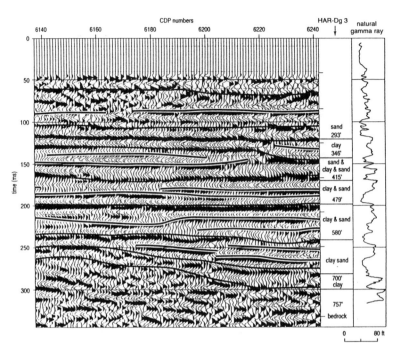

FIGURE 4.9   Seismic reflection profiling for geological variability.

Shallow seismic reflection profiles can provide a picture of geometric complexity and variability of contacts between different types of unconsolidated sediments and the sediment-bedrock interface. Based on a seismic study of the sediments overlying bedrock (depth of about 700 feet) at the Aberdeen Proving Ground in Maryland (Miller et al., 1996), the detail and horizontal interpretation confidence provided by shallow seismic profiles are not possible from drillhole data alone. Extrapolation of drill data from borehole to borehole required significant speculation and assumptions about lithologic correlations.

The seismic investigation was able to describe and detect subtle features of potential local hydrologic and geological significance, such as scour and infill patterns (horizontal expanse of less than 200 feet and vertical extent of less than 20 feet). The figure illustrates one of the seismic sections, which is correlated with lithologies determined from well logs. To even detect these features (and by no means to image them) with drilling methods would require closely spaced holes and significant expense. Seismic profiling proved to be a cost-effective method for interpolation between boreholes.

near-surface velocity anomalies), auxiliary use of the presence of diffractions from broken layers is sometimes needed to detect small offsets.

Stratigraphic studies can also be done successfully with shallow reflection, although the limits of resolution are debatable. Vertical resolution limit (seeing both top and bottom of a bed) is commonly described as a quarter-wavelength of the dominant frequency (Widess, 1973). In a practical sense, however, Miller et al. (1994) have shown that half-wavelength is sometimes a better (or at least more conservative) estimate of vertical resolution limit.

The water table usually presents a contrast in seismic wave velocity and a smaller contrast in density, both of which are likely to produce seismic wave reflections. Consequently, the detection of unconfined and perched water tables is often successful. Indeed, in some cases the water table reflection can be strong enough to make detection of slightly deeper reflectors difficult.

Applications in Which Shallow Reflection Sometimes Works. Shallow reflection seismology sometimes works in applications that require very high resolution, which necessitates both broad bandwidth and high frequencies. Because high frequencies usually fade rapidly or attenuate with increasing depth, the time window during which these applications work in a satisfactory manner is often quite small. Confidence in the validity of reflections usually increases at times >3 to 5 dominant-frequency cycles after the first break. In contrast, high frequencies are often lost at times greater than perhaps 150 to 200 ms. Consequently, the most commonly successful time window for the applications listed below is from 50 to 200 ms.

Detecting voids and tunnels is difficult, although a few occurrences are noted in the literature (e.g., Branham and Steeples, 1988; Miller and Steeples, 1991). There do not appear to be any examples of direct detection of voids using seismic reflection at depths exceeding 20 m. Robinson and Coruh (1988, p. 215) described a case of indirect detection of underground coal mining where reflections from times exceeding 120 ms are masked or attenuated by the presence of voids in coal seams.

Shallow reflection techniques can sometimes detect and delineate facies changes in the shallow subsurface. The detection of facies changes requires a high signal-to-noise ratio and expert interpretation skills. The facies changes often manifest themselves as subtle changes in amplitude or other seismic attributes loosely referred to as "seismic character." Occasionally, stratigraphic detail such as foreset beds on the scale of a few meters can be seen in deltaic deposits and other favorable environments. Intra-alluvial reflections can sometimes be seen on the scales of a few meters in thickness.

Delineation of beds thinner than a quarter-wavelength—based on the shape of the reflection wavelet—requires a higher-than-normal signal-to-noise ratio and substantial experience on the part of the interpreter (Widess, 1973).

Applications in Which Shallow Reflection Does Not Work. Currently, shallow
seismic reflection techniques appear unable to discriminate the interface between
two liquids in near-surface materials, such as between water and dense, nonaqueous-phase liquids (DNAPLs) or other chemicals. Modeling suggests that the
velocity contrasts at the interfaces may be too small to detect with current technology. Furthermore, frequencies at least an order of magnitude higher than those
available in shallow seismic reflection are needed to detect such chemical saturation lenses at the thicknesses commonly encountered in real-world pollution
situations.

Direct detection of tunnels or other voids at depths of 100 m or more with
surface-seismic reflection appears to be unlikely at this point. Cross-borehole
seismic methods, with their substantially higher frequencies, may be able to
detect voids a few meters across at these depths under favorable circumstances.

Improving Near-Surface Seismic Methods

Though relatively well established in petroleum exploration, the use of seismology for near-surface applications is still in an emerging state. Areas of potentially fruitful research and new applications follow.

• The combination of GRM refraction of the compressional wave (P-wave)
with the second body wave (S-wave) opens many new possibilities (Hasbrouck,
1987). For instance, various soil and rock mechanical parameters (e.g., Poisson's
ratio, Young's modulus, and shear modulus) can be determined from the combination of compressional wave velocity (Vp), shear wave velocity (Vs), and density (possibly derived from a gravity survey). These elastic constants can help
identify rock type and possibly fluid content of pore space (Domenico and
Danbom, 1987).

• The combination of GRM refraction of the compressional wave (P-wave)
with the second body wave (S-wave) also allows differentiation of "true" geometrical relative minima for the surface of a target refractor from artifacts of
overburden (soil) velocity variations. Confirmation of existence and correct position of relative minima is important in potentially locating DNAPL pools in the
subsurface (Brewster et al., 1995).

• Research is needed to compare VSP (vertical seismic profile) surveys
with those of shallow three-dimensional surveys. Multioffset, multiazimuth VSP
may have some advantages in resolution at many locations where boreholes are
available. Hole-filling pressurized bladders, which would allow the use of hydrophones at shallow depths above the water table, require further development. Hydrophones have some advantages over geophones because they are
less sensitive to the passage of non-P-wave modes and to distortional surface
waves.

• Three-component seismology at small-interval (<1 m) offsets is virtually nonexistent in the literature. Research in this area is necessary to examine the unaliased high-frequency components of the seismic wavefield, which could lead to improved use of shallow S-wave reflection and to simultaneous use of surface wave (both Love and Rayleigh) inversions to help constrain the near-surface velocity models. Such research could lead to a better understanding of anisotropy of the near-surface materials.

• Shallow (1- to 15-m depth) S-wave reflection seismology (e.g., Goforth and Hayward, 1992; Hasbrouck, 1993) is far from routine, but improvements could be of great assistance in engineering seismology, particularly for predicting amplification during earthquakes (Miller et al., 1986).

• When seismic P-wave reflection surveys are conducted, a large portion of other seismic information is unanalyzed. There is a need for collection and analysis of whole three-component seismograms that would also allow analysis of S-waves, mode converted waves, and Love waves.

• In the petroleum industry, time-varying reflection surveys are now being used to monitor reservoir conditions during hydrocarbon production, including following velocity variations within the reservoir induced by enhanced production procedures such as steam injection. Time-varying near-surface surveys could possibly be used to good advantage in a number of research applications. Birkelo et al. (1987) have shown that the top of the saturated zone can be monitored during a pumping test. Bachrach and Nur (1998) monitored tide-induced variations in near-surface velocity on an ocean beach in California. Jefferson and Steeples (1995) noted amplitude changes of 12 dB or more in reflection signals as soil moisture varies from about 18 to 36 percent by volume. Time-varying applications of near-surface seismic surveys in the future might include pre- and posttunnel construction to examine the effects of a tunnel's presence.

Some possible improvements involve seismic equipment and associated technologies including the following.

• There will always be a need for improved seismic sources. With the use of explosives becoming more difficult for various social reasons, the need for improved vibratory and impact sources will increase.

• One way to reduce the cost of data acquisition is to improve the speed of acquisition. Fifteen years ago the cycle time between shotpoints was about 20 seconds; today it is down to about 5 seconds. However, as the cycle time between shotpoints decreases, an attendant increase in the rate of geophone emplacement must occur. Consequently, there is a need to develop a way to rapidly or automatically plant geophones. One way to rapidly deploy geophones might be a draggable or automatically movable set of geophones, similar in concept to a hydroplane streamer used in marine applications but adapted for land applications. Such a low-frequency set of sensors has been used for several years by C. B. Reynolds Associates (Foster et al., 1992), but the primary challenge with their use is effective coupling to the ground to obtain the broader bandwidth and higher frequencies necessary for high-resolution near-surface applications.

• For many years, the seismic receivers of choice in reflection seismology have been velocity geophones. However, manufacturers' specifications sometimes do not reach to the high frequencies used in shallow reflection surveys. Consequently, an unbiased and independent research evaluation of receiver attributes of high-frequency geophones, following the work of Duff and Lepper (1980), could be useful. Tests should include amplitude, phase, spurious response analysis over a broad bandwidth, at least from 10 to 2 kHz. For shallow high-resolution purposes, accelerometers have become a possible alternative. Other motion-sensitive technologies may be applicable in the future.

REMOTE SENSING

Remote sensing offers unique observations of the earth's surface and shallow subsurface that complement conventional mapping and exploration methods. When employed in timely conjunction with field observations, remote sensing can be used to extrapolate local observations over extensive regional areas. A report summarizing remote sensing from satellite and aircraft (Watson and Knepper,1994) provides a comprehensive evaluation of the state of the art for geological mapping, mineral and energy resources, and environmental studies. It recognizes the evolution from aerial photography to multispectral systems that record solar reflected, thermal emitted, and radar illuminated radiation, and the emergence of imaging spectrometers, which acquire data with spectral resolution comparable to laboratory instruments. There are also several texts on remote sensing. A good source for explaining the physical basis is Elachi (1987); a report that summarizes many of the opportunities for remote sensing was issued by the National Research Council (NRC, 1995). An annual conference with published proceedings is sponsored by the Environmental Research Institute of Michigan and is a good source for current application focus. Technical instrument workshops on instruments are sponsored by the Jet Propulsion Laboratory, and substantial information and illustrative material are available on the Internet.

Aerial Photography

An ideal environmental remote-sensing system requires high spatial resolution, high sensitivity to changes in baseline characteristics, proven and accessible technologies, and low cost. Airborne photography, which is familiar and relatively inexpensive, is still ubiquitous in environmental studies despite obvious limitations—awkward archiving, lack of spectral resolution and sensitivity, and difficult integration with correlative geospatial data and digital technologies. Historical photos may provide evidence of waste sites and facilities that are now abandoned. Recent photography facilitates the analysis of current waste disposal practices and locations, drainage patterns, geological conditions, signs of vegetation stress, and other factors relevant to contamination site assessment. Additionally, aerial photograph fracture trace analysis is used at sites where bedrock contamination is a concern. Overlapping photo pairs can be used to model topography. Photography is gradually being replaced by digital image data, a trend that will be hastened as commercial satellites with spatial resolution in the 1- to 5-m range are launched in the next few years.

Multispectral Scanners

Multispectral scanners digitally record several images simultaneously at different wavelength bands. The bands are selected to exploit the greatest sensitivity to features of interest and allow significantly more definitive characterization of surface composition and state than does photography. The data are processed using computer image analysis algorithms based on physical or statistical models and knowledge of laboratory-measured physical properties. The most familiar system is the 30-m-resolution TM (Thematic Mapper) satellite instrument that has six reflectance channels (and a 120-m-resolution thermal channel). A number of aircraft systems are available to acquire additional spectral channels with comparable spectral resolution and somewhat higher ground resolution. Imaging radar, acquired as part of a national program is archived (along with photography from a similar program) at the U.S. Geological Survey's EROS Data Center. These data and their derivative images provide uniform spatial coverage, availability at different resolutions, and the digital format that are important for geographic information systems (GIS) analysis. Reflectance data have been successfully used to distinguish among geological units, to find hydrothermally altered rocks, to infer tectonic setting and local fold and fault structures, to map linear features that may indicate fracture controls, and to indirectly infer lithologic and structural information in heavily vegetated areas based on empirical correlations between vegetation type, density, distribution, and local geological conditions. Thermal infrared data can be used to map silicification and igneous lithologies, fractures, heat (due to near-surface exothermic reactions or underground coal fires), and changes in near-surface thermal properties and to examine surface water changes and groundwater discharge and seepage. Airborne and satellite radar provides all-weather weather capability to define terrain units, to map topographically expressed features that reflect local and regional geological structures, and in hyperarid terrain, to penetrate the upper meter or two.

Imaging Spectroscopy

Imaging spectrometry can be used to map minerals at the surface for a wide variety of environmental studies. An excellent example (see Plate 7) is the mapping by aircraft of acid-generating minerals at the Superfund site in Leadville,

Colorado (Swayze et al., 1996). Mine waste material is dispersed over a 30-km^2 area in which oxidation of sulfides releases heavy metals that are carried into the Arkansas River, a major source of water for urban centers and agricultural communities along the Rocky Mountain Front Range. The spectroscopy identified areas with higher acid-generating capacity based on the identification and mapping of distinctive zones of iron-bearing minerals.

Research Instruments

There are also a number of remote sensing instruments that have considerable promise for surface characterization but are not yet well established.

Passive Microwave Radiometry

Natural surfaces radiate mainly in the thermal infrared region; however, radiation at lower intensities extends throughout the electromagnetic spectrum into the submillimeter and microwave region. The radiant power emitted is a function of the surface temperature and its emissivity, which in turn are functions of surface composition and roughness. The large emissivity difference between ice and open water makes mapping polar ice cover and its change one of the most useful applications of microwave radiometry. The high dielectric constant (low emissivity) of water relative to most natural surfaces leads to applications involving mapping of soil moisture variation. However, because large variations can also result from differences in surface roughness or composition, repeat measurements are required to resolve ambiguities in interpretation. Microwave data can also be used to infer snow extent, onset of snowmelt, and water equivalent of snow. Limitations are the availability of data and the low spatial resolution. (For passive electromagnetic radiation, resolution is proportional to the ratio of receiver diameter to wavelength; thus, to preserve spatial resolution, very large receivers are required at longer wavelengths.)

Radar Interferometry

Radar interferometry from satellites can be used to detect minute changes in land surface geometry by comparing the phase difference between observations at two different times. Because the method is sensitive to differences as small as a few centimeters, it is sensitive to active faulting, subsidence caused by fluid withdrawal, pre-eruption volcanic swell, erosion, or tectonic creep. Atmospheric differences between the two observation times can cause substantial errors, and it is necessary that the surface has not been too greatly disrupted. This technique appears to have substantial potential for worldwide study of geological hazards once a good database and case history experience have been established.

Lasers

A number of experimental laser systems have been used from aircraft to illuminate the ground in order to measure surface conditions including surface texture, composition, elevation (decimeter accuracy), and water quality and depth (using fluorescence).

GEOCHEMICAL METHODS

Assessment of the subsurface geochemistry involves describing the chemical composition of solids, liquids, or gases. That is, the geochemistry of the subsurface may be defined as the chemical composition of bedrock and soil, groundwater and its dissolved or suspended load, and the atmosphere in the unsaturated zone. It is unlikely that all aspects of subsurface geochemistry can be determined remotely. In fact, relatively few chemical parameters can be readily detected without direct sampling and analysis. However, remote methods of chemical sensing for some constituents of interest in contaminated aquifer systems show promise.

Volatile Gas Emission

Wide use of organic solvents in the industrial and commercial sectors and of refined petroleum as fuels in numerous applications has led to nearly ubiquitous contamination of the environment with volatile organic compounds (VOCs) of a variety of compositions.

Volatilization at the surface of the water table and diffusion through the air-filled pore spaces in the vadose zone cause VOCs to be present at the surface overlying a contaminated site (see, for example, Figure 2.1). Soil-gas analysis became a popular screening tool for detecting VOCs during the 1980s. Soil-gas surveys can generate extensive chemical distribution data quickly at a fraction of the cost of conventional invasive methods and offer the benefits of real-time data. There are two types of soil-gas sampling. Grab sampling typically involves the insertion of a hand-held probe to depths of only tens of centimeters, with the volatiles pumped directly into a portable gas chromatograph. Passive sampling provides a measure of VOCs over time. It uses a sorbent material, such as activated carbon, that is placed below ground and later retrieved for analysis.

VOCs and gases can also be important as indicators of biological degradation reactions proceeding at depth. Isotopic information on these gases, obtained through mass spectroscopic methods in the laboratory, may yield even more information about the nature and extent of biodegradation reactions occurring within an aquifer.

Water Composition

Ground water moves into, through, and out of a given portion of the shallow subsurface. In doing so, reactions occur among the components of the aquifer system (water, minerals, atmosphere, and associated biota) that can lead to a change in the composition of the groundwater. Sampling the groundwater in wells or springs downgradient of the site may allow inferences to be made about a portion of the subsurface that we cannot sample directly. That is, the composition of the dissolved or suspended load in the groundwater may be used as an indicator of the composition of the solids, liquids, and gases in the study area, as well as of the reactions they are undergoing. (Many of the principles are similar to the geochemical water sampling developed in ore deposit exploration.) Tracers may be passive or natural products of the environment, or they may be introduced purposefully for the purposes of sampling. Natural or artificial tracers may be introduced and sampled without disturbing the physical integrity of the study site. Analysis of the outcome is by traditional chemical methods in the field or the laboratory.

Most solutes in natural and contaminated groundwater are ionic; that is, they are present as charged cations and anions in solution. Dissolved ions can carry an applied electrical current; if they are present in high enough concentrations in groundwater, noninvasive electrical geophysical methods can detect their presence and location. An example of a useful and successful application is in the mapping of saltwater intrusion fronts in coastal water supply aquifers. Fresh groundwater has highly contrasting electrical properties to the intruding seawater, and because of density differences and poor mixing in a porous medium, the contact between the two types of water can be fairly sharp and, in these cases, relatively easily detected and mapped.

Another widespread problem is the presence of plumes of landfill leachate within an otherwise clean groundwater system. Electrical methods can map such plumes as well as their migration because the leachates are typically high in dissolved salts and metals and contain a variety of organic compounds. Similarly, acid mine drainage can also be mapped because of high concentrations of dissolved solids and metals. Significant challenges remain in detecting nonionic contaminants, including many dissolved organic compounds such as pesticides.

Composition of the Solid Phase

Remote assessment of the chemical composition of the subsurface's solid portions (soil and bedrock) is problematic. Relatively few material properties that can be remotely measured yield information about the chemical composition of solid materials, although the presence of some minerals can be modeled. One approach to the composition would be to use a combination of the knowledge of site geology with geophysical determinations of density or porosity contrasts to support an interpretation of rock type, but this does not go much beyond what a geologist can do without noninvasive technologies. A metallic object can be detected from the surface through the contrast of its electrical or magnetic properties with the enclosing silicate, carbonate, or oxide rock, but little specific knowledge can be gained about chemical composition. Use of self potentials and induced polarization methods potentially could be applied to such chemical determinations.

Radioactive Methods

Detection of natural radioactivity (or that resulting from disposal of radioactive materials) can be of use in characterizing the shallow subsurface. Applications include, for example, regional mapping, prospecting for some minerals, and detection of leaking storage facilities containing radionuclides. The same properties that make radionuclides dangerous also make them easy to track in the environment. "The Multi-Agency Radiation Survey and Site Investigation Manual (MARSSIM) provides a nationally consistent consensus approach to conducting radiation surveys and investigations at potentially contaminated sites" (Environmental Protection Agency, 1997). The manual describes well-tested methods and details the specific methodology and analysis that should be used. Several other aspects of radioactivity that can be valuable in site characterization involve invasive (e.g., borehole logging [Ellis, 1987]) or direct sampling (e.g., tritium or bomb-pulsed chlorine tracers in subsurface water).

GEOBIOLOGICAL METHODS

Properties of the biota of most interest to site characterization biologists may be the most difficult to determine noninvasively. The identity, abundance, diversity, and ecology of the resident organisms, as well as their overall physiological status, are the most important general properties to assess.

Biological processes in the near surface ultimately depend on the genetic makeup of the near-surface biota, which in turn depends on physical and chemical environmental factors that select the biota at a given site. Generic properties of the biota (identity, abundance, diversity, and ecology and their overall physiological status and activity) will be important in most site characterizations. However, given the spatial variability and heterogeneity of geological settings, large variations in metabolic activities may occur across a given site. For example, a process such as aerobic respiration of a pollutant chemical (or biomineralization) depends upon the availability of oxygen, which itself can be controlled by water content, inorganic oxidation-reduction reactions, and content of exchangeable organic compounds. The pollutant chemical itself may be more or less available for respiration depending on its solubility in water, its octanol-water partition coefficient, its organic matter content, or competition with soil particle surface adsorbers. Finally, the total abundance of aerobic heterotrophic organisms controlled by oxidizable organics will greatly influence the oxygen available for respiration of the pollutant.

Presently there are no noninvasive methods for direct measurement of biological presence or metabolic activity in the near surface. However, in some geological settings, subsurface biological activity can be inferred indirectly from near-surface biogeochemical activity, which might be measurable using noninvasive methods. For example, near-surface biogeochemical activity in the vicinity of oil reservoirs has been mapped by electrical resistivity methods (Sternberg, 1991), and airborne imaging spectroscopy has been used to detect and map biogenic minerals in acid and neutral drainage areas of acidified watersheds (see Plate 7). Minimally invasive methods such as soil-gas analysis by gas chromatography, chemical assays of bioaccumulating plants, and bacterial indicator culturing of surface soil have been used to a limited extent for petroleum and mineral exploration as well as environmental pollution studies. Noninvasive technologies show some promise in biological assessments, but until more research is done to develop other methods, the characterization of site biology will still depend to a large degree on analysis of samples obtained by invasive methods. Development of coordinated noninvasive and minimally invasive methods for geobiological site characterization remains a challenge (e.g., Ghiorse, 1997).

REFERENCES

Annan, A. P., M. L. Brewster, J. P. Greenhouse, J. D. Redman, G. W. Schneider, G. R. Olhoeft, and K. A. Sander, 1992. Geophysical monitoring of DNAPL migration in a sandy aquifer, *62nd Annual International Meeting, Society of Exploration Geophysicists, Expanded Abstracts 62,* 344-347.

Bachrach, R., and A. Nur, 1998. High-resolution shallow-seismic experiments in sand, Part I: Water table, fluid flow, and saturation, *Geophysics 63,* 1225 1233.

Bell, R. E., 1997. Gravity gradiometry resurfaces, *The Leading Edge 16*(1), 55-59.

Bertin, J., and J. Loeb, 1976. *Experimental and Theoretical Aspects of Induced Polarization,* Vols. I and II, Gebruder Borntraeger, Berlin-Stuttgart.

Birkelo, B. A., D. W. Steeples, R. D. Miller, and M. A. Sophocleous, 1987. Seismic-reflection study of a shallow aquifer during a pumping test, *Ground Water 25,* 703-709.

Blakely, R. J., 1996. *Potential Theory in Gravity and Magnetic Applications,* Cambridge University Press, Cambridge, 441 pp.

Bradford, J., M. Ramaswamy, and C. Peddy, 1996. Imaging PVC gas pipes using 3-D GPR, *Proceedings of the Symposium on the Application of Geophysics to Engineering and Environmental Problems, Environmental and Engineering Geophysical Society,* Wheat Ridge, Colorado, pp. 519-524.

Branham, K. L., and D. W. Steeples, 1988. Cavity detection using high-resolution seismic reflection methods, *Mining Engineering 40,* 115-119.

Brewster, M. L., A. P. Annan, J. P. Greenhouse, B. H. Kueper, G. R. Olhoeft, J. D. Redman, and K. A. Sander, 1995. Observed migration of a controlled DNAPL release by geophysical methods, *Groundwater 33,* 977-987.

Buker, F, A., G. Green, and H. Horstmeyer, 1998. Shallow 3-D seismic reflection surveying: Data acquisition and preliminary processing strategies, *Geophysics 63,* 1434-1450.

Burger, H. R., 1992. *Exploration Geophysics of the Shallow Subsurface,* Prentice-Hall, Englewood Cliffs, N.J.

Butler, D. K., 1984. Interval gravity-gradient determination concepts, *Geophysics 49*(6), 828-832.

Davis, J. L., and A. P. Annan, 1989. Ground-penetrating radar for high-resolution mapping of soil and rock stratigraphy, *Geophysical Prospecting 37*(5), 531-552.

Domenico, S. N., and S. H. Danbom, 1987. Shear-wave technology in petroleum exploration—Past, current, and future, in *Shear-Wave Exploration,* S. H. Danbom and S. N. Domenico, eds., Society of Exploration Geophysicists Special Publication.

Duff, B. M., and C. M. Lepper, 1980. A high-resolution controlled-source audiomagnetotelluric system for mining applications, *50th Annual International Meeting, Society of Exploration Geophysicists,* Reprints, 80, Session:E.8.

Elachi, C., 1987. *Introduction to the Physics and Techniques of Remote Sensing,* John Wiley & Sons, New York, 413 pp.

Ellis E. V., 1987. *Well Logging for Earth Scientists,* Elsevier, New York, 532 pp.

Ellis, R. G., and S. W. Oldenburg, 1994. The pole-pole 3-D dc-resistivity inverse problem: A conjugate-gradient approach, *Geophysical Journal International 119,* 187-194.

Environmental Protection Agency (EPA), 1997. Multi-Agency Radiation Survey and Site Investigation Manual, EPA-402-R-97-016 (www.epa.gov/rpdweb00/marssim/filestoc.htm).

Fisher, E., F. A. McMechan, A. P. Annan, and S. W. Cosway, 1992. Examples of reverse-time migration of single-channel ground-penetrating radar profiles, *Geophysics 57,* 577-586.

Foster, M. S., K. R. Nunn, S. A. Lewis, and D. J. Reynolds, 1992. Zero phasing seismic data without wells offshore W. Africa: Reducing uncertainty and variability of the wavelet, *62nd Annual International Meeting, Society of Exploration Geophysicists, Expanded Abstracts 92,* 241-243.

Fullager, P. K., 1984. A uniqueness theorem for horizontal loop electromagnetic frequency soundings, *Geophysical Journal, Royal Astronomical Society,* 559-566.

Ghiorse, W. C., 1997. Subterranean life, *Science 275,* 789-790.

Goforth, T., and C. Hayward, 1992. Seismic reflection investigations of a bedrock surface buried under alluvium, *Geophysics 57*(9), 1217-1227.

Greaves, R. J., D. P. Lesmes, M. J. Lee, and M. N. Toksoz, 1996. Velocity variations and water content estimated from multi-offset, ground-penetrating radar, *Geophysics 61*(3), 683-695.

Greenhouse, J., M. Brewster, G. Schneider, D. Redman, P. Annan, G. Olhoeft, J. Lucius, K. Sander, and A. Mazzella, 1993. Geophysics and solvents: The Borden experiment, *The Leading Edge 12,* 261-267.

Hasbrouck, W. P., 1987. Hammer-impact, shear-wave studies, in *Shear-Wave Exploration,* S. H. Danbom and S. N. Domenico, eds., Society of Exploration Geophysicists Special Publication.

Hasbrouck, J. C., 1993. An Integrated Geophysics Program for Non-Intrusive Characterization of Mixed-Waste Landfill Sites, U. S. Department of Energy, DOE Contract No. DE-AC04-86ID12584.

Henson, H., and J. L. Sexton, 1991. Premine study of shallow coal seams using high- resolution seismic reflection methods, *Geophysics 56,* 1494-1503.

Hinze, W., 1994. Engineering and environmental applications of gravity and magnetic methods, in *Introduction to Applied Geophysics: Short Course,* Environmental and Engineering Geophysical Society.

Hinze W. J., R. L. Roberts, and D. I. Leap, 1990. Combined analysis of gravity and magnetic anomaly data in landfill investigations, in *Geotechnical and Environmental Geophysics, Vol. II: Environmental and Groundwater,* S. H. Ward,, ed., Society of Exploration Geophysicists, Investigations in Geophysics #5, pp. 267-272.

Huggenberger, P., E. Meier, and A. Pugin, 1994. Ground-probing radar as a tool for heterogeneity in gravel deposits: Advances in data processing and facies interpretation, *Journal of Applied Geophysics 31,* 171-184.

Jakeli, C., 1993. A review of gravity gradiometer survey system analyses, *Geophysics 58*(4), 508-514.

Jefferson, R. D., and D. W. Steeples, 1995. Effects of short-term variations in near-surface moisture content on shallow seismic data, 65th Annual International Meeting, Society of Exploration Geophysicists, *Expanded Abstracts 95*, 419-421.

Jol, H. M., and D. G. Smith, 1991. Ground penetrating radar of northern lacustrine deltas, *Canadian Journal of Earth Sciences 28*, 1939-1947.

Keller, G. V., and F. C. Frischknecht, 1970. *Electrical Methods in Geophysical Prospecting*, Pergamon Press, Oxford.

Killham, K. 1994. *Soil Ecology*, Cambridge University Press, New York.

Knoll, M. D., F. P. Haeni, and R. J. Knight, 1991. Characterization of a sand and gravel aquifer using ground-penetrating radar, Cape Cod, Massachusetts, in U.S. Geological Survey Toxic Substances Hydrology Program, Water Resources Investigations (USGS-WRI-91-4034), Reston, Virginia.

Koefoed, O., 1979. *Geosounding Principles, I: Resistivity Sounding Measurements*, Elsevier, New York

Lankston, R. W., 1988. High resolution refraction seismic data acquisition and interpretation, in Environmental Geophysics, Society of Exploration Geophysicists Special Publication.

Lankston, R. W., and M. M. Lankston, 1986. Obtaining multilayer reciprocal times through phantoming, *Geophysics 51*, 45-49.

Li, Y., and D. W. Oldenburg, 1994. Inversion of 3D dc-resistivity data using an approximate inverse mapping, *Geophysical Journal International 116*, 527-537.

Madden, T. R., and Cantwell, 1967. Induced polarization: A review in mining geophysics, BE Soc. Exploration Geophysics.

Mellett, J. S., 1996. Location of human remains with ground-penetrating radar, in *Fourth International Conference on Ground-Penetrating Radar, Special Paper 16*, Geological Survey of Finland, pp. 359-365.

Miller, R. D., and D. W. Steeples, 1991. Detecting voids in a 0.6-m coal seam, 7 m deep, using seismic reflection, in *Geoexploration 28*, 109-119.

Miller, R. D., S. E. Pullan, J. S. Waldner, and F. P. Haeni, 1986. Field comparison of shallow seismic sources, *Geophysics 51*, 2067-2092.

Miller, R. D. S. E. Pullan, D. W. Steeples, and, J. A. Hunter, 1994. Field comparison of shallow P-Wave seismic sources near Houston, Texas, *Geophysics 59*, 1713-1728.

Miller, R. D., J. Xia, J. Swartzel, J. Llopis, and P. Miller, 1996. High-resolution seismic reflection profiling at Aberdeen Proving Grounds, Maryland, in *SAGEEP '96*, Environmental and Engineering Geophysical Society, Wheat Ridge, Colorado, pp. 189-201.

Mooney, H. M., 1977. *Handbook of Engineering Geophysics*, Bison Instruments.

Niwas, S., and M. Israil, 1987. A simple method for interpretation of dipole resistivity soundings, *Geophysics 52*, 1412-1417.

National Research Council (NRC), 1994. *Airborne Geophysics and Precise Positioning: Scientific Issues and Future Directions*, Board on Earth Sciences and Resources, National Academy Press, Washington, D.C., 111 pp.

NRC, 1995. *Earth Observations from Space: History, Promise, and Reality*, Space Studies Board, National Academy Press, Washington, D.C., 310 pp.

NRC, 1997. *Satellite Gravity and the Geosphere: Contributions to the Study of the Solid Earth and Its Fluid Envelope*, Board on Earth Sciences and Resources, National Academy Press, Washington, D.C.

Oldenburg, D. W., and Y. Li, 1994. Inversion of induced polarization data, *Geophysics 59*, 1327-1341.

Olhoeft, G. R., 1986, Direct detection of hydrocarbon and organic chemicals with ground penetrating radar and complex resistivity, in *Proceedings of the NWWA/API Conference on Petroleum Hydrocarbons and Organic Chemicals in Ground Water—Prevention, Detection and Restoration,* National Water Well Association (NWWA), Dublin, Ohio, pp. 284-305.

Palmer, D., 1980. *The Generalized Reciprocal Method of Seismic Refraction Interpretation,* Society of Exploration Geophysicists Monograph.

Parker, R. L., 1984. The inverse problem of resistivity sounding, *Geophysics 49,* 2143-2158.

Pekeris, C. L., 1940. Direct method of interpretation in resistivity prospecting, *Geophysics 5,* 31-46.

Pelton, W. H., L. Rijo, and C. M. Swift, Jr., 1978. Inversion of two-dimensional resistivity and induced polarization data, *Geophysics 63*(4), 788-803.

Redpath, B. B., 1973. Seismic Refraction Exploration for Engineering Site Investigation, National Technical Information Service.

Roberts, R. L., W. J. Hinze, and D. I. Leap, 1990a. Application of the gravity method to the investigation of a landfill in glaciated midcontinent, U. S. A., in *Geotechnical and Environmental Geophysics, Vol. II: Environmental and Groundwater,* S. H. Ward,, ed., Society of Exploration Geophysicists, Investigations in Geophysics #5, pp. 253-260.

Roberts, R. L., W. J. Hinze, and D. I. Leap, 1990b. Data enhancement procedures on magnetic data from landfill investigations, in *Geotechnical and Environmental Geophysics, Vol. II: Environmental and Groundwater,* S. H. Ward,, ed., Society of Exploration Geophysicists, Investigations in Geophysics #5, pp. 261-266.

Robinson, E. S., and C. Coruh, eds., 1988. *Basic Exploration Geophysics,* John Wiley & Sons, New York, 562 pp.

Shi, W., and F. D. Morgan, 1996. Non-uniqueness in self-potential inversion, *66th Annual International Meeting, Society of Exploration Geophysicists, Expanded Abstracts 66,* 950-953.

Simms, J. E., and F. D. Morgan, 1992. Comparison of four least-squares inversion schemes for studying equivalence in one-dimensional resistivity inversion, *Geophysics 57,* 1982-1293.

Slichter, L. B., 1933. The interpretation of resistivity prospecting method for horizontal structures, *Physics 4,* 307-322.

Stam, J. C., 1962. Modern developments in shallow seismic refraction techniques, *Geophysics 27*(2), 198-212.

Sternberg, B. K., 1991. A review of some experience with the induced-polarization/resistivity method for hydrocarbon surveys: Successes and limitations, *Geophysics 56,* 1522-1532.

Sternberg, B. K., 1997. The LASI high-frequency ellipticity system, in *Proceedings of the High-Resolution Geophysics Workshop,* Tucson, Arizona.

Sternberg, B. K., and M. M. Poulton, 1997. High Resolution Subsurface Imaging and Neural Network Recognition: Non-Intrusive Buried Substance Location, DOE Report on Contract DE-AC21- MC 29 101 A001.

Stokoe, K. H., S. G. Wright, S. A. Barg, and J. M. Roësact, 1994. Characterization of geotechnical sites by SASW method, in *Geophysical Characterization of Sites,* R. D. Woods, ed., Oxford & 1BH Publishing Co., pp. 15-25.

Sumner, J. S., 1976. *Principles of Induced Polarization for Geophysical Exploration,* Elsevier Scientific Publishing Co.

Sutinen, R., P. Hanninen, R. Cromwell, and E. Hyvonen, 1992. GPR and dielectric classification of glacial materials, in *Fourth International Conference on Ground-Penetrating Radar, Special Paper 16,* Geological Survey of Finland, pp. 133-138.

Swayze, G. A., R. N. Clark, R. M. Pearson, and K. E. Livo, 1996. Mapping acid-generating minerals at the California Gulch Superfund site in Leadville, Colorado using imaging spectroscopy, *Summaries of the 6th Annual JPL Airborne Earth Science Workshop.*

Telford, W. M., L. P. Geldart, and R. E. Sheriff, 1990. *Applied Geophysics,* Cambridge University Press, New York.

Tripp, A. C., G. W. Hohmann, and C. M. Swift, Jr., 1984. Two-dimension al resistivity inversion, *Geophysics 49*, 1708-1717.

Vacquier, V., C. R. Holmes, P. R. Kintzing, and M. Laverone, M., 1957. Prospecting for ground water by induced electrical polarization, *Geophysics 22*, 660-687.

Wait, J. R., ed., 1959. *Overvoltage Research and Geophysical Applications*, Pergamon Press, London.

Ward, S. H., B. K. Sternberg, D. J. LaBrecque, and M. M. Poulton, 1995. Recommendations for IP research, *The Leading Edge 14*, 243-247.

Watson, K., and D. H. Knepper, eds., 1994. *Airborne Remote Sensing for Geology and Environment—Present and Future*, U.S. Geological Survey Bulletin 1926, 43 pp.

White, D. J., 1989. Two-dimensional seismic refraction tomography, *Geophys. J. 97*, 223-245.

Widess, M. B., 1973. How thin is a thin bed? *Geophysics 38*, 1176-1180.

Wurmstich, B., and F. D. Morgan, 1994. Similarities in modeling groundwater flow and dc resistivity, *64th Annual International Meeting, Society of Exploration Geophysicists, Expanded Abstracts 94*, 578-579.

Wurmstich, B., D. F. Morgan, G. P. Merkler, and R. L. Lytton, 1991. Finite element modeling of streaming potentials due to seepage: Study of a dam, *61st Annual International Meeting, Society of Exploration Geophysicists, Expanded Abstracts 91*, 542-544.

Young, R. A., J. M. Forgotson, L. White, D. O'Meara, Z. Deng, Z. Liu, C. L. Liner, R. Weindel, and S. H. Danbom, 1995. The OCAST project: Integrated geophysical characterization assisting flow simulation, *65th Annual International Meeting, Society of Exploration Geophysicists*, extended abstract.

Yule, D. E., M. K. Sharp, and D. K. Butler, 1998. Microgravity investigations of foundation conditions, *Geophysics 63*(1), 95-103.

Zhang, J., and M. N. Toksoz, 1998, Nonlinear refraction traveltime tomography, *Geophysics 63*, 1726-1737.

Zhang, J., R. L. Mackie, and T. Madden, 1995. 3-D resistivity forward modelling and inversion using conjugate gradients, *Geophysics 60*, 1313-1325.

Zohdy, A. A. R., 1989. A new method for the automatic interpretation of Schlumberger and Wenner sounding curves, *Geophysics 54*(2), 245-253.

5

Interpretation

In characterizing a site, existing data often guide the specific methodology of additional data collection and should be integrated with the newly collected information. This integration is part of the modeling process. Modeling also includes the interpretation of data from specific instruments prior to integration efforts. Model output can be visualized to check for consistency as well as for presentation to the client.

REVIEW OF EXISTING DATA

Efforts to examine and interpret the near-surface portion of the earth usually involve multiple types of data. In addition to basic geographic map data, there are usually some geologic and hydrological data initially available, at least on a regional scale. Perhaps there might be some geophysical data that were collected for a particular project at a nearby location. One or more boreholes also may be available, often including natural gamma radiation and electrical resistivity logs.

These various types of auxiliary data may be of unknown and variable quality, and collected with instruments often of unknown calibration. Even nearby "ground-truth" borehole data may not be very useful or reliable. Not all descriptions of sample cuttings from a drilling operation are equally useful—for example, some observations may have treated changes in color as the most important attribute rather than grain-size observations, which are technically more valuable.

Hence, before interpretation is begun a *critical review* must be done of all existing data. This review serves to identify gaps and errors in the existing data, which can be addressed in subsequent field efforts. Data gaps may occur when data are not sampled often enough in space or time to prevent aliasing, as mentioned briefly in the seismology section of Chapter 4. A common example of aliasing occurs in western movies when the wheels on a forward-moving buggy appear to spin backward because the visual field is not sampled often enough to represent the true picture. Consequently, data review should include consideration of the adequacy of the sampling, with respect to the project objectives, for each type of data.

The process of assessing data to identify errors and omissions requires close attention to detail and is a laborious effort. A solution is to use well-trained and experienced people who are able to focus upon basics and are sensitive to the fact that errors and omissions can and do occur. Complex statistical methods or sophisticated computer imaging cannot substitute for invalid or missing data.

One of the most common methods of data display in two dimensions is through the use of contouring. Although human interpretive contouring is often difficult to beat in the geologic sense, machine contouring algorithms are now routinely used to prepare displays of geological and geophysical data, especially structural contour maps and potential field data maps. More recently, three-dimensional displays of seismic data have been used to beneficial effect (e.g., Dorn, 1998).

Multiple sources of data must be used to confirm site-specific conditions. When measurements by different methods agree, our interpretations will have a higher level of confidence. By virtue of redundancy, this process also provides a secondary form of quality assurance for individual sets of data, offering a reliable, defensible means of testing the hypothesis embedded in the conceptual site model.

DATA INTEGRATION

When a single geophysical method is used to survey a complicated site, it usually is possible to create multiple models of the subsurface that fit the resulting data. Another method, measuring different phenomena, will produce a different set of plausible models. In most cases, the intersection of the two sets of possible models is a smaller set that reduces the number of possible interpretations. More surveys that measure even more phenomena will further constrain the interpretation. In an ideal case, enough data will be collected to produce a unique geologic or hydrologic model. In many cases, ground-truth data from boreholes and outcrops can be used to calibrate the geophysical parameters and result in model interpretation with a higher degree of confidence.

Most site characterization projects use several types of geophysical measurements and sources of data. Data from each of these measurements often are interpreted in isolation; when this occurs, such data are neither integrated (a process sometimes called data fusion) nor interpreted simultaneously with data from other techniques. In those cases where an attempt is made to combine data

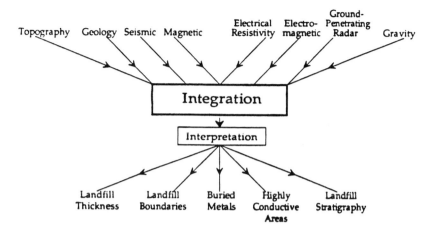

FIGURE 5.1   Schematic diagram of the concept of integrating geologic information and data from diverse geophysical methods for determining properties of a landfill. (After Roberts et al., 1989.)

sets, the data may be integrated and interpreted in only a qualitative fashion. Intrinsic relationships among different types of data often are uninvestigated, setting the stage for conflicting and irreconcilable interpretations.

Successful site characterization often combines several different objectives and requires multiple measurements. Combining data from numerous methods might help resolve ambiguities and prevent faulty interpretation of individual measurements. In data interpretation it is important to take advantage of complementary and redundant information in all available data from a site (see Figure 5.1). However, because data can be combined and manipulated in so many ways, the end user or client (e.g., the site manager) is often confused, with no guide to determine the meaning of the composite results.

Data integration should consider all of the data, not just geophysical data, acquired during a site characterization. Multiple sources of data provide the ability to check the quality of individual data sets against each other. Data integration also provides an estimate of the statistics involved in characterizing a site and the uncertainty in the overall solution. Each observation contains an associated error, and each data set is the result of a statistical distribution in space and/ or time.

If disparate data sets are mapped into some common equivalent space, they should overlap. If not, a closer examination of the possible measurement or processing errors may be needed. For example, using Poisson's relation, it is possible to transform a magnetic map into a "pseudogravity" map by assuming some value of magnetic susceptibility for rock materials below the earth's surface. If the resulting pseudogravity map does not resemble an actual gravity map, one can assume that the magnetic susceptibility used in the calculation was not correct.

Seismic, magnetic, electrical, gravity, and GPR signals arise from different subsurface physical parameters. The data can be inverted to obtain three-dimensional estimates of the constitutive properties of the ground. However, because the data sets arise from different physical properties, the various data sets cannot be readily combined *before* inversion. Data integration, then, is most often performed after cross-sectional, areal, or three-dimensional maps of the intrinsic physical properties uncovered by each of the imaging methods have been prepared. The process is iterative; each data set is reinterpreted, taking into account interpretation from other data sets until a consistent interpretation is obtained.

For example, information obtained from GPR can be compared with that obtained from shallow seismic reflection, both of which are based on wave propagation. When different methods provide complementary information at a particular site, combining the data is likely to provide more information than using any one method alone. The use of shallow, high-resolution seismic reflection techniques in concert with GPR has the potential to assist in characterizing sites in environmentally sensitive areas.

Seismic and GPR techniques measure different physical parameters, but as shown in Figure 5.2, the two techniques can yield consistent results. At other sites, the two techniques might respond to changes in different regions of the subsurface and not yield a consistent interpretation. Seismic reflections arise from changes in acoustic impedance, that is, the product of seismic wave velocity and density must change for a seismic reflection to occur. If seismic velocity increases by the same amount that density decreases at a given interface, no seismic reflection is produced from the interface. An example occurs in salt deposits, which commonly do not yield good seismic reflectors at internal interfaces.

Ground penetrating radar, on the other hand, responds to changes in the constitutive electrical parameters (permittivity and conductivity) of the subsurface. If either of these electromagnetic parameters changes at the interface used in the example given above, a radar reflection may occur where no seismic reflection would occur. Imagine an opposite example where the constitutive parameters are constant across an interface at which either bulk density or seismic wave velocity varies. In sum, seismic data and GPR data tell us about different physical parameters of the earth material being surveyed and often can be used to compare each other's results.

Important geologic and hydrologic interfaces often represent changes in properties that include density, seismic velocity, electrical conductivity, and dielectric permittivity. Knowledge of these four parameters enhances the possibility of predicting fluid flow paths, particularly in fractured media. For example, seismic velocity usually decreases in fracture zones, and radar wave velocity may increase in these same fracture zones, particularly when a large increase in air-filled pore space is involved. Conversely, where a fracture and the pore spaces are filled with precipitated minerals, seismic waves may propagate more quickly and radar waves more slowly. Clay tends to attenuate radar energy, whereas seismic energy often is not attenuated rapidly by propagation in clays. At other sites, seismic waves might be attenuated rapidly in dry, quartzitic sand, whereas radar waves propagate well in the same medium.

Depending on local geologic and hydrologic conditions certain types of stratigraphic variation may be detectable directly (by the presence of a reflection), indirectly (by the disruption of some other reflector), or not at all. The presence or absence of a reflection can also depend on the seismic or radar parameters used (see Figure 5.3). The absence of evidence of an seismic or GPR reflection is not necessarily evidence of the absence of a stratigraphic variation.

Analysis of both elastic and radar-frequency electromagnetic survey data with densely spaced measurements is essential to the construction of a high-quality subsurface image. Although a variety of field procedures has been used to produce such coverage in individual seismic and GPR surveys, little is known about how the two techniques might practicably be combined in very high resolution site characterization surveys.

In the same set of data it is possible to show large differences in the resolution and accuracy of features depending on a priori assumptions about what is in the subsurface. Therefore, inappropriate visualization of data and integration of multiple sources of data could be misleading. Developing the process of data integration requires considerable future research. How do we integrate disparate data sets from geophysics, geochemistry, hydrology, and biology, and map the multidimensional data into an integrated solution? What kind of statistics should be used, and what levels of confidence are required? Further investigation of such questions is needed to optimize data integration and interpretation.

MODELING

Models based on an understanding of physical, chemical, and biological properties and processes (in contrast to those based on empirical correlation) are of great value in the effective use of noninvasive methods in site investigations. Numerical models can provide linkages between the phenomena being measured and the properties and processes occurring in the earth. They provide tools for optimizing survey design, quantifying uncertainties and limitations associated with data acquisition, and validating interpretations. There are many existing numerical models that are potentially useful, but they should be catalogued, documented, and made user friendly and easy to locate to fulfill their potential.

Our understanding of, and ability to exploit, a particular characterization phenomenon can be improved by an iterative process involving the following approaches: (1) empirical (observation of an apparent relationship between the phenomenon and a property or process of interest), (2) analytical (experimental

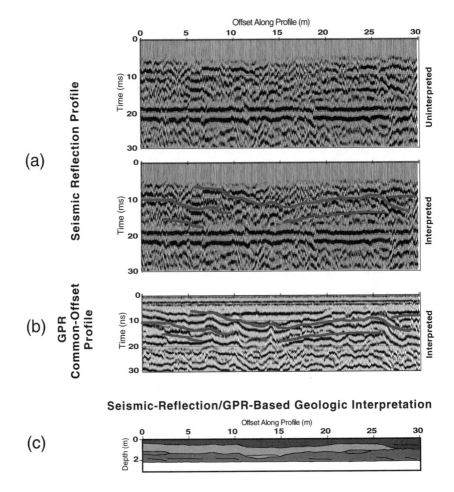

Seismic Reflection Profile

GPR Common-Offset Profile

(a)

(b)

(c)

Seismic-Reflection/GPR-Based Geologic Interpretation

and theoretical research to explain the relationship), and (3) numerical (computer models of cause and effect, which can be useful in a predictive sense). If models are well designed and easy to use, they (1) make analytical expertise available to practitioners, (2) enable conceptual understanding of the relationships between the phenomenon and the properties or processes, and (3) help practitioners and clients understand the capabilities and limitations of the measurements.

In addition, rigorous numerical models can be used to improve the quality and reliability of nonintrusive site characterization surveys. During survey design, numerical models can be used to help choose the characterization method, quantify the anticipated signal and noise, and optimize the proposed survey parameters. Processing and interpretation make extensive use of computer models,

FIGURE 5.2   An example of qualitatively merged geophysical imaging of the shallow subsurface. (a) An uninterpreted and interpreted seismic reflection profile along a 30-m transect in the Arkansas River alluvial valley ~1 km southeast of Great Bend, Kansas. Geophone spacing was 10 cm and the seismic source was a 22-caliber rifle with subsonic short ammunition fired 10 cm downhole. (b) A common-offset GPR profile using a 225 MHz antenna coincident with the seismic profile. The seismic interpretation is overlain on the GPR section. (c) Geological interpretation of the 30 m transect created by merging the individual interpretations of the seismic and GPR data and adjusting coincident reflectors. The three main layers, from top to bottom, represent the Platte series soil profile, an unstratified medium sand (bound on the top by an erosional unconformity), and a cross-stratified medium sand to medium gravel with various bounding surfaces (identified as individual lines on the interpretation). The interpretation was field constrained by a nearby ~2-m-deep hand-dug hole. At −2.1 m is the top of the saturated zone, constrained by a nearby monitoring well. The water table is easily identified on the seismic section but absent on the GPR section (possibly related to the diffuse nature of the boundary relative to the GPR wavelength). Although not quantitatively "fused" by some inversion technique, the coincident profiling using seismic and GPR methods improved the detail and confidence of the interpretation. Figure courtesy of Gregory S. Baker, 1999, University of Kansas).

especially for inversion techniques. For critical (e.g., hazardous) sites, the most important use of models is to validate interpretations and do quantitative sensitivity analyses.

Models, whether physical, chemical, geological, or hydrological, must be mathematically validated by use of easily verifiable cases. One way to do this is to compare results for cases that have known analytical solutions. Another way to analyze models is to use sensitivity analysis (e.g., McElwee and Yukler, 1978) in which the response of a model is examined in terms of the mathematical derivatives of the constitutive equations.

VISUALIZATION

An important advance of recent years is in the visualization of geophysical data. Previously, data were usually presented as measured field values, corrected for drift with other simple corrections. For example, with electrical and electromagnetic data, a common form of data processing is still to normalize to apparent resistivity or apparent conductivity, which simply matches the data to a homogeneous earth model. Plotting the data in "pseudosection" form using simple guidelines provides depth interpretation. The impact of this presentation is limited; an experienced interpreter usually is needed to convert these plots to a geologic model of the earth. Interpretation with such displays usually consists of locating

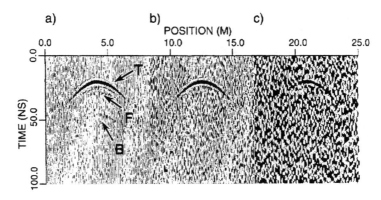

FIGURE 5.3   Visibility of GPR reflections decreases as the signal-to-noise (S/N) ratio increases; (a) is for S/N of 15.0, (b) for S/N of 7.5, and (c) for S/N of 1.5. T is the reflection from the top of a buried tank, B from the bottom of the tank, and F from a fluid (air/gasoline) interface inside the tank. Figure is from Zeng and McMechan (1997).

anomalies ("bump hunting") and ascribing geologic significance. These presentations can be misleading because pseudodepth may not be true depth and data artifacts might appear as geologic features.

Advances in modeling, inversion, and visualization now make it possible to present data in a geologically and visually meaningful way. Shaded relief maps, for instance, have revolutionized the presentation of potential field data (e.g., Plate 3). The shaded surface can reveal features that may be invisible when displayed using contouring or simple pseudocolor. Color presentations also convey a great deal of information to users and often enable easier recognition of significant features. However, with the introduction of displays that are pleasing to the eye comes the danger of misleading viewers—a change of color scale or rendering can often completely alter the significance an interpreter places on a feature. It is incumbent on the individuals presenting the data that their presentation conveys as accurately as possible the actual geology or geologic process. Error estimates should be displayed with each presentation, along with alternative displays.

In addition to visualization of the subsurface, the data can be integrated with many other types of data about the site's location (e.g., transportation networks, population, ecosystems, topography, resources, land-use, and other locationally referenced themes) using geographic information systems (GIS). When integrated within a GIS context, models or "what-if" scenarios can be tested for use in a broader decision-making process.

RECOMMENDATION

Scientists and engineers must improve their ability to integrate multidisciplinary data for modeling, visualizing, and understanding the subsurface.

The interpretation of characterization data has both creative and quantitative components. The creative component consists of conceiving all of the possible geologic models likely to explain the data; the quantitative component involves generating synthetic data for every possible model to demonstrate whether a particular model is consistent with the field data. Generating multiple synthetic data sets from a single geologic model, although not done routinely, is technically feasible. It requires only the development of modeling codes based on an accepted set of programming standards. Conceiving a geologic model that will fit multiple data sets is much more difficult. Advances in this area will include both technical (e.g., simultaneous inversion) and human (e.g., studies of team dynamics) elements.

Interpretations of any set of multiple measurements will be strengthened, and ambiguity reduced, if they are the result of early integration and simultaneous inversion of diverse data types. The following areas of research are needed to improve the efficacy and rigor of data fusion and integrated interpretation:

• Develop a better understanding of the coupling and interactions among the physical, chemical, and biological properties and processes that affect the measurements done in characterization surveys.

• Develop integrated models that allow simultaneous modeling of simulated data sets from several multiple surveys over a single geologic model.

• Based on the understanding of physical, biological, and chemical properties and processes, develop mathematical tools and computer programs that are able to perform simultaneous, quantitative inversion of multiparameter data sets.

• Create three-dimensional scientific visualization tools and techniques that will allow human interpreters to monitor the inversion process, assess the resulting geologic models, and improve the quality of the interpretation.

In the area of modeling, a variety of needs can be identified:

• Many numerical modeling programs currently exist in universities and government laboratories. However, some are obscure, are difficult to use, and require computing facilities not readily available to many practitioners. Major benefits can be achieved in a short time by adapting existing codes to "standard" computing platforms and by adding interfaces that make them easy for the average practitioner to find and use.

• Numerical models become, in effect, "expert advisers" to the practitioners who use them. In some cases they have great influence because of the human tendency to believe what comes out of a computer. Therefore, it is important that the expertise embedded in numerical models be up-to-date and correct. Appropriate regulatory agencies or professional societies should establish a program of certification of numerical models to be used in site characterization surveys.

• Some phenomena have not yet been modeled; others have been modeled with so many simplifying assumptions that the models often are not realistic. Universities and government laboratories should be encouraged and supported to identify deficiencies and develop rigorous computer models that provide realistic descriptions of subsurface properties and processes.

• Given the need for data fusion and integrated interpretation, universities and government laboratories also should be encouraged to develop and validate integrated modeling software explicitly designed for site characterization.

• To facilitate the broader use of computer modeling there should be a clearinghouse or repository to (1) facilitate discovery of available modeling software; (2) provide standard data sets against which codes and models can be tested; and (3) assist the private, academic, and government sectors in developing training curricula in the use of computer modeling.

REFERENCES

Baker, G. S., 1999. Seismic Imaging Shallower than Three Meters, Ph.D. dissertation, Department of Geology, The University of Kansas, Lawrence, 320 pp.

Dorn, G. A., 1998. Modern 3-D seismic interpretation, *The Leading Edge 17*, 1262-1272.

McElwee, C. D., and M. A. Yukler, 1978. Sensitivity of groundwater flow models with respect to variations in transmissivity and storage, *Water Resources Research 14*, 451.

Roberts, R. L., W. J. Hinze, and D. I. Leap, 1989. A Multi-techniques geophysical approach to landfill investigations, in *Proceedings of the Third National Outdoor Action Conference on Aquifer Restoration, Ground Water Monitoring, and Geophysical Methods*, National Water Well Association, Dublin, Ohio, pp. 797-811.

Zeng, X., and G. A. McMechan, 1997. GPR characterization of buried tanks and pipes, *Geophysics 62*(3), 797-806.

6

Nontechnical Issues

Subsurface characterization is an essential component of many environmental and engineering applications. If noninvasive methods are to become an important component of subsurface characterization, a number of issues, which have little to do with the state of technology or the availability of competent geoscientists and engineers, have to be addressed. Similar nontechnical issues are discussed in two recent reports (Federal Facilities Policy Group, 1995; National Research Council, 1997).

This chapter explores a variety of nontechnical barriers to the application of noninvasive technologies to characterize the subsurface environment. Insufficient economic incentives are a major impediment to the effective use of modern noninvasive technology. Legal and institutional constraints also can be impediments to the effective use of noninvasive methods. These constraints include statutory and regulatory requirements, health and safety concerns, and the nature of standards and certification procedures. These impediments have the potential to inhibit creativity and discourage the development of effective solutions to site-specific problems. In some cases, institutional pressures and other demands can take precedence over scientific and technical judgments concerning a site, and this can be compounded by lack of information, misunderstandings, or misconceptions on the part of one or more of the stakeholders involved (contractors, clients, regulators, and the public).

INCENTIVES

Researchers in the resource industries, federal laboratories, and universities have made significant advances in both instrumentation and methodologies. However, few of these innovations have found their way into routine practice in near-surface characterization. In a related area, a 1997 NRC report (*Innovations in Ground Water and Soil Cleanup: From Concept to Commercialization*) assessed various reasons for the difficulty in applying innovations to environmental cleanup. These reasons include lack of market stimulation, information, technology testing, and cost comparisons. Similar nontechnical impediments appear to apply in the area of noninvasive technologies. According to the 1997 NRC report (pp. 7-8), "Lack of information has contributed to the slow transfer of new ideas for remediation technologies from the laboratory to the field and from one site to another. Technology reports are often incomplete and lacking in critical scientific evaluation and peer review. Reliable cost data are also lacking, Moreover, much information on prior experiences with remediation technologies is proprietary."

A company faced with the responsibility of a hazardous waste cleanup might choose the needed site characterization and remediation methods on the basis of what will satisfy regulatory and legal requirements at minimum cost (NRC, 1997). When dealing with a problem such as hazardous waste, in situ sampling is often required in designing cleanup methods. In such a case, many involved with a project may have the perception *that noninvasive site characterization adds cost without commensurate benefit* and that the added cost will not be recovered during the life of the project. Alternatively, some contractors have invested in a particular characterization method and often rely almost exclusively on this capability. They may be reluctant to consider other characterization methods because of possible additional capital investment and/or the need to subcontract these methods. As such, the clients' perception of added costs of noninvasive characterization can be reinforced by many contractors' reliance on a specific, often invasive, technique.

A key to greater use of noninvasive characterization is to demonstrate net economic benefits. The oil industry, for example, is quick to make large investments in new technologies because even small improvements in exploration and production can significantly improve revenue and profit. Although the oil industry developed three-dimensional seismic methods over twenty years ago, these methods remained little more than a research curiosity for at least a decade. During that time three-dimensional seismic images became widely used to guide drilling, and three-dimensional seismic reflection surveys are now the standard procedure for major oil companies and many independent oil companies. For example, ARCO averaged fewer than three three-dimensional seismic surveys per year during 1980 to 1982, but it averaged nearly 40 such surveys per year in 1993 to 1995 (Dorn, 1998). The costs of research and development for the three-dimensional seismic methods and the costs of more extensive data collection efforts in the field were more than offset by the savings associated with fewer dry holes; there have been unsubstantiated claims of success ratios of over 80 percent.

The economic benefits of noninvasive methods in resource exploration and recovery are apparent. For an engineering or environmental application, the use of properly evaluated and designed noninvasive characterization can have two benefits: the overall cost of the program can be reduced (due to the difference in cost between noninvasive characterization and drilling), and the invasive sampling points can be chosen to give maximum information (see Figure 4.9).

Noninvasive methods have the potential to reduce characterization costs. In many cases, noninvasive characterization provides comparable information at a cost that may be less than that of intrusive techniques such as drilling. In some cases, intrusive methods (e.g., drilling or digging) can engender major financial and environmental risks that can be avoided with noninvasive technologies. For example, a major oil company in Texas was faced with financial penalties relating to a refinery unless a leakage mitigation plan was developed quickly for a chemical storage pond. Drilling on approximately 50-m centers revealed the presence of, but did not delineate, a buried bedrock valley. A seismic reflection survey at the site sampled the subsurface at 0.7-m intervals, delineating two buried valleys, which enabled the refinery operator to develop a contingency plan that satisfied the state regulatory agency (Miller et al., 1989). As another example, inadvertent disruption during construction of buried utility cables and gas pipelines is frequently in the news; noninvasive characterization might help avert such disruptions and their associated costs (National Transportation Safety Board, 1997).

Documentation of these benefits in the public domain is rare, and therefore, the cost-effectiveness of noninvasive characterization is difficult to establish. Most of the literature concerning noninvasive characterization emphasizes technical developments. However, useful information about such economic benefits exists in related areas and could be made available.

Government agencies, environmental and engineering contractors, and university researchers should work to analyze and document the potential costs and benefits of the use of noninvasive characterization methods in a wide variety of applications. There is a large amount of data (in the form of government-funded projects) that could be subjected to analyses, and an evaluation of alternative scenarios could demonstrate the potential benefits of noninvasive characterization. Documenting these benefits can demonstrate possible economic incentives for the use of noninvasive technologies in site characterization efforts.

OPERATIONAL CONCERNS

To be effective, subsurface characterization efforts should have the flexibility to design for site-specific conditions and to change or modify the characterization program as results become available. However, certain laws such as Superfund and the Resource Conservation and Recovery Act (RCRA) "provide a disincentive to change the selected remedy even if a much better solution evolves" (NRC, 1997; see Box 6.1). Other nontechnical impediments to the application of noninvasive characterization arise from concerns related to (1) regulations, (2) standards of performance, (3) health and safety, and (4) institutional barriers.

BOX 6.1
Innovation and Regulations

The regulatory structure for implementing hazardous waste cleanups, especially at Superfund and Resource Conservation and Recovery Act (RCRA) sites, has added to the inherent difficulties that remediation technology vendors face in bringing new products to the market. The fundamental problem of these programs is that they rely on regulatory push rather than market pull to create demand. The process of technology selections is strictly regulated....Providers of new technology have trouble staying in business while awaiting client and regulatory acceptance of their processes...

The Superfund and RCRA corrective action programs leave little room for customer (or consultant) choice and no room for a "try as you go" concept. Regulators must "sign off" on the customers choice of a technology through an official Superfund record of decision or RCRA corrective action plan. Mechanisms for adjusting the remedy once it is officially approved are bureaucratically cumbersome and provide a disincentive to change the selected remedy even if a much better solution evolves. [pp. 46-47]

In the private-sector market, inadequate cost containment has decreased the incentives for selecting innovative technologies. Often federal remediation contractors are placed on "auto pilot" after being awarded the cleanup contract on a cost-reimbursable basis, so there is little incentive for cost-effectiveness (GAO, 1995). According to an audit by GAO [General Accounting Office] (1995), cost overruns are common to remediation efforts at federal sites, due in part to inadequate oversight of contractors. GAO found evidence of fraud, waste, and abuse by federal remediation contractors (GAO, 1995). With no incentive to reduce costs, there is no incentive to search for new solutions. [pp. 55]

SOURCE: *Innovations in Ground Water and Soil Cleanup: From Concept to Commercialization* (NRC, 1997).

One or more of these impediments have been experienced by committee members while conducting or examining site characterization programs; others in the characterization community have expressed related experiences (e.g., Freeze and Cherry, 1989). Similar concerns are discussed in reports of the Federal Facilities Policy Group (1995) and the NRC (1997).

Regulations

Regulatory requirements may inhibit flexibility (NRC, 1997). Both contractors and regulators have a vested interest in adopting and following detailed, rigid, generic regulatory requirements regardless of site-specific conditions. If they can show that they followed every regulation to the letter, contractors have some protection from lawsuits regardless of the quality of their results. Regulators can similarly protect themselves by trying to cover every possible eventuality with a regulation. These approaches can lead regulators to require—and contractors to provide—subsurface characterization programs that are *regulation driven rather than solution driven*.

Practitioners may satisfy regulatory criteria at the expense of sound professional practice. Decisions are legally correct if the regulations are followed, and practitioners cannot afford the risk of deviating from the regulations.

At present, requests for proposals and contracts for shallow subsurface characterization often prescribe methods and survey designs without consideration of site-specific conditions. Contractors or consultants with vested interests in certain technologies or geographic regions may be tempted to encourage regulators and clients to continue this practice to avoid competition.

To maximize the net benefits achieved from investments in federal facilities cleanup, the Federal Facilities Policy Group (1995) recommended (1) more rigorous risk-based priority setting and management oversight, both within and across sites; and (2) statutory and regulatory reforms to remove impediments to success. The report argues that regulators often specify *how* a site is to be characterized (i.e., what data should be collected by the specified technique) rather than specifying the overall *objectives* of the characterization effort. For example, if a regulator required that a ground penetrating radar (GPR) survey be done at a site, the presence of a subsurface clay layer could make GPR less useful than electrical methods at the same site (see Plate 6). To provide the flexibility necessary to deal with such situations, regulations should specify *how* such decisions are to be made at each site rather than attempting to specify *what* the decisions should be. The Environmental Protection Agency's (EPA) Office of Solid Waste and Emergency Response began in 1997 to implement a program called the Performance-Based Measurement System (PBMS) that aims to reduce the burden on the regulated community associated with the use of new site characterization and monitoring techniques. The objectives of PBMS are to improve data quality, reduce the cost of compliance by lowering regulatory barriers, and stimulate the development and use of innovative monitoring technologies (*www.epa.gov/ooaujeag/notebook/pbms.htm*). Under PBMS, EPA would no longer prescribe the use of specific technologies but would specify an acceptable data quality level, which serves as a criterion for technology users to select the appropriate site characterization or monitoring techniques.

Standardized Practices

Laws and regulations may encourage or require the implementation of standardized practices in site characterization, which offers some liability protection to practitioners. Standardized practices usually assume some consistency in problems and conditions. However, each site has unique conditions and problems that require site-specific considerations. The choice of characterization methods, design of the

TABLE 6.1   Examples of Standard Approaches for Site Characterization

Organization	Effort
American Society of Testing and Materials (ASTM, 1997)	Accelerated Site Characterization Committee D-18 on Soils and Rocks
U.S. Environmental Protection Agency (EPA)	Superfund Accelerated Cleanup Model
EPA Office of Underground Storage Tanks (EPA, 1997)	Tools for Expedited Site Characterization
Department of Energy (DOE), Ames Laboratory	Expedited Site Characterization
DOE, Argonne National Laboratory	Expedited Site Characterization (QuickSite)
California Environmental Protection Agency	Environmental Technology Certification Program

data acquisition program, and interpretation of results will be different for each site. This situation makes it difficult to develop generally accepted "best practices."

Conflicts between scientific and technical issues and legal and regulatory concerns often beset site characterization projects. A high priority of the client (or owner of the site) is to ensure that all applicable laws and regulations are satisfied fully so that decisions and actions can be defended in court, if necessary. To achieve this objective, a "cookbook" approach is often followed, which may limit the flexibility needed to assess certain site-specific considerations. If clients can demonstrate that the prescribed procedures were implemented faithfully, they may be protected from legal action even if the results are less than optimal.

The engineering community is generally comfortable working with a structure of relevant certification and standardized approaches. Several groups (see, Table 6.1) have developed or are developing standard approaches or guidance to site characterization. These standard approaches are designed to promote proper techniques for site characterization and reduce the possibility of questionable site characterization practices.

Incidences of questionable practices (Shuirman and Slosson, 1992), which could be called charlatanism, misuse, and fraud, led the Society of Exploration Geophysicists (SEG) to amend its charter to exclude corporate membership from companies whose practices were not based on accepted scientific principles. The SEG amended its constitution to say, "The services or products provided must be demonstrably based upon accepted principles of the physical sciences" (SEG Constitution, Article III, Section 9). Upon adoption of this language, several companies were asked to disassociate themselves from the SEG. Such actions help raise the level of credibility of characterization efforts.

Subsurface characterization programs should be customized for every site to achieve specific objectives within financial and time constraints. Some tools exist to assist nonexperts in the design and justification of such customized efforts. For example, the Geophysics Advisor Expert System (Olhoeft, 1992) can help select the appropriate geophysical tools to apply to EPA Superfund site problems. However, the details of such efforts should be planned and executed by multidisciplinary teams that may include geophysicists, geologists, chemists, geochemists, geotechnical engineers, biologists, and others as required to achieve the site-specific objectives. Relevant disciplines should be represented from the outset of a major project, and members of the team should understand and adhere to a common set of decision-making processes and standards.

Government agencies (federal, state, and local) need to develop approaches to site characterization that focus on flexible, program design procedures and decision-making processes that account for the unique character of each site.

Design and decision-making processes and procedures should achieve a balance between accountability and flexibility. Highly constrained procedures ensure accountability, but they can inhibit the implementation of programs customized to the unique characteristics of the site. Removing constraints ensures flexibility at the expense of accountability. Standardizing and documenting the structure and rationale behind the decision-making processes can provide legally defensible characterization programs that are well suited to the unique problems of a given site. Successful implementation will require that decision-making processes be peer-reviewed and certified and that universities offer academic programs that teach the processes as well as the technical foundation.

Health and Safety

Site characterization activities involve collection of data in the field and have some associated hazards related to worker safety and health; these can be quite varied. (Hazards related to the possible spread of contaminants from invasive sampling are addressed earlier in this report.) For noninvasive field methods, the hazards can be as simple as tripping and falling or as complex as those associated with using explosives. For explosive hazards the perceived risk can sometimes stop or alter the nature of seismic measurements.

Seismic experimentation often uses explosive charges because of the wide bandwidth of the energy spectrum of vibrations these sources produce. In large-scale petroleum exploration, the explosives are extremely safe to handle but still produce large energy releases that can be dangerous. Near-surface seismics often use smaller explosive sources, similar to those contained in large-gauge shotgun shells that are detonated using a modified shotgun (Miller et al., 1986). The shotgun-shell explosive source is relatively safe to handle, ship, and use. Yet many individual sites often limit the use of such relatively benign explosive seismic sources.

Site-specific rules that may inhibit the use of such common explosive charges generally fall into two categories—weapons or fire. For weapons, a site might have rules that prohibit firearms. Exception to this policy may be difficult to obtain even when the actual practice involves augering a hole and shooting a specialty rifle into the hole for the sole purpose of exciting elastic vibrations. With pressures on site managers to adhere to stringent safety rules, such permission is often hard to get.

Regarding the issue of fire, the concern of those in authority is more understandable. Even though the shotgun-shell source is a contained explosion in an augered hole that is a few feet deep, there is a small possibility that the explosion could start a fire. Therefore, if flammable materials are present on-site, it is difficult to receive permission to use small explosive devices.

As a result of such site-specific rules, seismic sources such as weight drops are often used instead of explosives. These alternative seismic sources are often adequate for the task, but in other cases, they are less than optimal and may not be able to produce the characterization objectives.

Institutional Barriers

A broad category of institutional barriers, discussed in a report by the Federal Facilities Policy Group (1995), includes statutory decisions, competitiveness and infighting among agencies and contractors, the "not-invented-here" syndrome, and "turf" protection.

A relatively recent example of a congressionally mandated program involved buried UXO and mine detection advanced technology demonstration (ATD; U.S. Army Environmental Center, 1994). The statutory provisions of the ATD program specified where the demonstration was to be conducted, which agency was to manage the demonstration, and technical details constraining the demonstration. The ATD was funded at approximately $30 million over a three-year period (1994-1996). Congress reacted to the complex technological requirements by attempting to specify the "solution," requiring off-the-shelf-technology demonstrations in the form of a contractor competition. The ATD program was prompted by the recognition of UXO and mine detection as an extremely high-priority issue and a desire to find the nonexistent "silver bullet" (see Box 6.2).

Several important elements were not included in the program. There was no comprehensive site characterization in advance of the ATD. No phenomenological predictions or assessments of results were conducted. Results reported by

---

BOX 6.2
UXO Detection and Lack of Universal Solutions

Because of the enormity and diversity of the UXO problem, there is not a single technological "silver bullet" that will provide a universal solution. Detection solutions include aggressive investigations of a variety of sensor technologies, singly and in combination and a thorough understanding of the signatures of UXO and the cluttered environments in which they are located.

SOURCE: Joint Unexploded Ordnance Clearance Steering Group, 1997.

---

various contractors were not complete enough to allow a detailed phenomenological assessment (Altshuler et al., 1995; Butler et al., 1998). Details of the UXO and mine types and locations were not released to contractors or other government agencies, which would have allowed independent assessments and contractor self-evaluations.

Competition among agencies, turf protection, and the not-invented-here syndrome can lead to major inefficiencies and barriers to effective subsurface characterization programs. A 1996 NRC report (*Barriers to Science: Technical Management of the Department of Energy Environmental Remediation Program*) identified many of these barriers as factors that have hindered environmental restoration efforts of the Department of Energy's Office of Environmental Management. In addition, the Federal Facilities Policy Group (1995) reported similar barriers in an assessment of complex environmental restoration programs. This assessment found that not only is there competition among agencies, but there is also potential for overlapping regulatory authorities between state and federal governments that can lead to inefficient site characterization efforts (e.g., see Box 6.3). Because of the pressures often involved in subsurface characterization and environmental remediation, agencies might attempt to redefine their mission areas and develop programs to address these problems.

INFORMATION AND COMMUNICATION

As with most areas of emerging technologies, transfer of research advances into applications poses a challenge (i.e., closing the gap between the state of knowledge and the state of the practice). With noninvasive characterization methods, such transfer presents a two-pronged challenge. One is to ensure that advances in techniques and methods are communicated to the practitioners of characterization efforts; the other challenge involves the clients or owners of the site that is being characterized and those that set and enforce regulations.

Practitioners are typically contractors (e.g., consulting firms or individuals)

BOX 6.3
Conflicting Approaches

...uncertainties are compounded by the potential overlay of one regulatory authority upon another. States have invoked their authority under RCRA or state law at
Superfund sites, and in some cases have imposed additional requirements beyond those required under CERCLA [Comprehensive Environmental Response,
Compensation and Liability Act]. Conversely, a site that is being remediated under
a state RCRA or other program may be subject to listing on the NPL [National
Priorities List] under CERCLA, introducing a different regulator and different cleanup criteria.

SOURCE: Federal Facilities Policy Group (1995; Section 4.C.2)

that provide characterization services to clients that have a site-specific need. In
most situations the consulting (service) firms that do near-surface characterization are small (an order of magnitude or more smaller than similar service firms
in the oil industry) and are often specialized in their applications and techniques.
Practitioners should have an in-depth knowledge of the various methods involved—theory, data acquisition, and processing and interpretation—and an understanding of how to design and carry out multidisciplinary characterization
surveys. However some contractors that would like to use noninvasive tools may
find it difficult to stay abreast of developments in one specialty, let alone multiple
fields or integrated design and interpretation. The gap between the state of knowledge and the state of practice in noninvasive methods may be due, in large part, to
a lack of awareness on the part of the practitioners.

Scientists and engineers need to place greater emphasis on com-
municating information about noninvasive tools and techniques and
their recent advances to practitioners.

Limitations of time, money, and personnel make it difficult for contractors to
stay current about the latest tools and techniques being developed in universities
and government laboratories. This problem can be addressed by efforts that make
such information more easily located and readily available. The rapid growth of
use of the Internet and the World Wide Web helps to solve the distribution
problem (see Box 6.4); the challenge is to develop a process and mechanisms
whereby unbiased assessments of new developments can be validated and posted
in a timely fashion.

Competition (by bidding) for characterization jobs, compounded by regulatory pressures and legal liability, can discourage the adoption of new tools and
techniques unless contractors (1) have access to documentation of the methods'

BOX 6.4
Internet Site Characterization Resources

Sources of information on innovative site characterization technologies are available through the following Internet sites:

- Characterization, monitoring, and sensor technologies: www.cmst.org
- Consortium for site characterization HREF=""
- Environmental technology verification program: www.epa.gov/etv

---

applicability and acceptability, (2) have information to help them persuade clients that the benefits will justify the costs, and (3) can get the training they need to implement the new methods. These issues could be addressed by development of an aggressive continuing education program to distribute information about the capabilities and use of the new tools and techniques. However, to be effective in the competitive environment in which near-surface contractors operate, delivery of the continuing education programs must be independent of time and location. Again, the Internet and the World Wide Web offer opportunities for new approaches to continuing education.

Clients, practitioners, and regulators have varying levels of need to understand the science and technology underlying the various physical, chemical, and biological measurements that can be made to investigate the shallow subsurface (see Box 6.5). To bridge the possible differences in scientific and educational backgrounds, it is important to communicate what is actually measured, how it relates to the desired parameter, and what the probability of success will be. In this way, expectations are appropriately adjusted, and the best noninvasive method(s) can be selected to achieve the desired goal. For example, GPR was used with limited success in an attempt to locate pieces of ValuJet Flight 592 that crashed in May 1996 and was buried in the muck of the Florida Everglades. Investigators expected to locate metal pieces; however, GPR does not measure

---

BOX 6.5
Keeping Current

With the emergence of an enormous number of new site assessment tools recently, regulators are often hard pressed to keep current with the latest technologies and maintain their other duties of reviewing site assessments, evaluating corrective action plans, and/or issuing regulations.

SOURCE: EPA, 1997

---

metal directly. Instead, GPR responds to changes in electrical properties (dielectric and conductivity). The success of GPR depends on how it is applied, how the results are interpreted, and whether what GPR measures can be related successfully to the desired measurement goal (in this example, metal pieces).

The committee encourages government agencies and professional societies to form partnerships in long-term efforts to distribute and share information on the capabilities and recent developments of noninvasive characterization methods.

Possibilities include the following:

• Develop a series of "handbooks," organized according to characterization methods, that document their applicability and limitations and provide sources of information about the latest tools and techniques.
• Develop simplified decision support materials that practitioners can use to identify the most appropriate and most modern techniques to consider in solving a particular problem.
• Support the establishment of an on-line resource center where information about new tools and techniques can be distributed efficiently.
• Encourage development of continuing education programs that utilize the latest advances in distance learning and on-demand access to information.

The users (clients) of the results of noninvasive subsurface characterization are seldom geoscientists or engineers. Results of noninvasive characterization are inherently nonunique and sometimes cannot address certain classes of subsurface characterization requirements (e.g., contaminant concentrations). The users' expectations of unique and definitive answers often make the results of subsurface characterization seem suspect. This suspicion can be reinforced when results are presented with realistic error (accuracy) estimates, statements of nonuniqueness, and assessments of resolution. This problem requires effort from all parties to understand, educate, and communicate effectively.

Geoscientists and engineers performing noninvasive site characterizations should strive to understand the purpose and potential application of the characterization and attempt to present the results in a form that is understandable and applicable by the users. Users likewise should attempt to bridge the gap by being aware of the limitations and uncertainties associated with subsurface characterization.

Because most of today's problems require multidisciplinary solutions, more cross-disciplinary education is necessary. Although research areas have become highly specialized, practitioners require a general knowledge of many disciplines. They also should understand the importance of knowing and using structured design and decision-making processes, and they should be able to codify and defend the thought processes used to arrive at a particular decision. The educational system should meet both needs—the narrow, in-depth focus of the researcher and the general, multidisciplinary need of the practitioner. There is a need to inform regulators, decision makers, and the public about the capabilities and limitations of noninvasive methods.

Efforts are needed to examine the effectiveness of the following in addressing many of the educational concerns: (1) university curricula and research programs; (2) continuing education programs, particularly using distance learning technologies; and (3) public outreach programs.

REFERENCES

American Society for Testing and Materials (ASTM), 1997. Provisional Standard Guide for Expedited Site Characterization of Hazardous Waste Contaminated Sites, ASTM: PS 85-96.

Altshuler, T. W., A. M. Andrews, R. E. Dugan, V. George, M. P., and D. A. Sparrow, 1995. Demonstrator performance at the unexploded ordnance advanced technology demonstration at Jefferson Proving Ground (Phase I) and implications for UXO clearance, IDA Paper F-3114, Institute for Defense Analyses, Alexandria, Virginia.

Butler, D., E. Cespedes, K. O'Neill, S. Arcone, J. Llopis, J. Curtis, J. Cullinane, and C. Meyer, 1998. Overview of science and technology program for JPG Phase IV, *Proceedings of the UXO Forum 98*, Anaheim, California.

Dorn, G. A., 1998. Modern 3-D seismic interpretation, *The Leading Edge 17*(9), 1262-1272

Environmental Protection Agency (EPA), 1997. *Expedited Site Assessment Tools for Underground Storage Tank Sites: A Guide for Regulators*, EPA Office of Underground Storage Tanks, EPA-510-B-97-001, Washington, D.C.

Federal Facilities Policy Group, 1995. *Improving Federal Facilities Cleanup*, Council on Environmental Quality and Office of Management and Budget, Washington, D.C. (www1.whitehouse.gov/WH/EOP/OMB/html/miscdoc/iffc-2.html).

Freeze, A., and J. Cherry, 1989. What has gone wrong?—A guest editorial, *Groundwater 27*(4).

General Accounting Office (GAO), 1995. *Federal Hazardous Waste Sites: Opportunities for More Cost-Effective Cleanups*, GAO/T-RCED-95-188, Washington, D.C.

Joint Unexploded Ordnance Clearance Steering Group, 1997. *Unexploded Ordnance Clearance: A Coordinated Approach to Requirements and Technology Development, Report to Congress*, Office of the Under Secretary of Defense (Acquisition and Technology), March 1997.

Miller, R. D., S. E. Pullan, J. S. Waldner, and F. P. Haeni, 1986. Field comparison of shallow seismic sources, *Geophysics 51*, 2067-2092.

Miller, R. D., D. W. Steeples, and M. Brannan, 1989. Mapping a bedrock surface under dry alluvium with shallow seismic reflections, *Geophysics 54*, 1528-1534.

National Research Council (NRC), 1996. *Barriers to Science: Technical Management of the Department of Energy Environmental Remediation*, National Academy Press, Washington, D.C.

NRC, 1997. *Innovations in Ground Water and Soil Cleanup: From Concept to Commercialization*, National Academy Press, Washington, D.C.

National Transportation Safety Board (NTSB), 1997. *Protecting Public Safety Through Excavation Damage Prevention*, Safety Study NTSB/SS-97/01, Washington, D.C., 106 pp.

Olhoeft, G. R., 1992. Geophysics Advisor Expert System (version 2.0): *U.S. Geological Survey Open-File Report 92-526*, 21 pp. and floppy disk.

Shuirman, G., and Slosson, J.E., 1992. *Forensic Engineering: Environmental Case Histories for Civil Engineering and Geologists*, Academic Press, San Diego, California, 296 pp.

U. S. Army Environmental Center (USAEC), 1994. Unexploded ordnance advanced technology demonstration program at Jefferson Proving Ground (Phase I), Report No. SFIM-AEC-ET-CR-94120, U.S. Army Environmental Center, Aberdeen Proving Ground, Maryland.

7

Realizing Future Capabilities

During the past two decades, advances in computing and microelectronics have stimulated the production of an impressive array of tools and techniques for noninvasive characterization of the shallow subsurface. These advances have made existing tools and techniques faster, cheaper, or more effective. However, there have been relatively few fundamental innovations with regard to the phenomena being observed or the sensing devices that convert those phenomena into electrical signals. Additional research and development (R&D) is needed to enhance and extend current capabilities, to develop fundamentally new measurements, and to close the aforementioned gap between the state of the practice and the state of knowledge.

Some of R&D areas are short-term (e.g., 3 to 5 years) opportunities for advances that can be achieved using existing knowledge and technologies—in other words, enabling the state of the practice to be closer to the state of the art. These include the automation of tools and techniques and the development of methods for monitoring properties, processes, and temporal variations. Others are of a long-term (e.g., 10 to 20 years), high-risk nature, but they offer the potential to enhance significantly our ability to "see into the earth." The long-term needs deal primarily with the discovery of fundamentally new phenomena that can provide information about subsurface conditions and the development of new sensing techniques for making measurements at a distance. In this section, the recommendations for R&D are presented in order from short term to long term.

The resource industries (particularly oil) have invested heavily in R&D because they are profit driven; breakthroughs in exploration can dramatically increase profits. In comparison to the gross expenditures on characterization efforts, the near-surface characterization industry invests relatively little in R&D.

The committee believes that lack of investment results because site characterization activities do not generate revenue for the client but are required in a wide range of environmental and engineering situations. In this situation, R&D is often a cost without commensurate short-term benefits. This is exacerbated by the "low-bid" nature of most specific site characterization efforts (Shuirman and Slosson, 1992), a situation not likely to change. As a result, the private sector usually defers needed R&D in favor of activities that produce more immediate benefits in the form of cost reduction. As such, the committee believes that it is in the interest of the nation to increase the federal government's investment in R&D and to provide incentives and mechanisms for increased private sector investment. Finally, because much of the research is based in universities and federal laboratories, it will be important to provide for effective communications between researchers and industry to ensure that both short-term and long-term R&D products are of great value to the near-surface characterization industry.

Government agencies should be encouraged to increase their investment in near-surface characterization R&D in the areas appropriate to their mission.

For example, this includes:

• Agencies (e.g., the Department of Defense and the Department of Energy) that are required to deal with near-surface problems (hazardous waste, construction, etc.) at their own sites;
• Agencies (e.g., the Environmental Protection Agency, the Department of the Interior, the Department of Transportation, and the U.S. Army Corps of Engineers) responsible for oversight of the environment, resource development, transportation, and infrastructure where near-surface characterization can be an integral part of their business; and
• Agencies for which basic research either is their primary mission (e.g., the National Science Foundation) or is critical to their mission (e.g., the U.S. Geological Survey).

In addition, research programs supported by federal agencies should take advantage of advisory boards to ensure that R&D expenditures are producing innovations that will be of value to the site characterization process.

The federal government already supports some of the R&D that is needed to deal with proliferating societal issues ranging from land mines to hazardous waste to underground construction. A mechanism should be developed to stimulate private sector investment in R&D in spite of the cost-driven nature of the industry and its size (usually small consulting firms) and application-specific nature.

Government and industry should cooperatively investigate mechanisms for coordination and support of site characterization research.

One possible mechanism is a quasi-governmental entity that could be empowered to collect funds from site characterization contractors and clients. On the other hand, the site characterization industry may have special characteristics that demand an entirely new model. Initially it would be useful to define the needs and characteristics of the industry (particularly the economic structure) prior to designing a solution that optimally meets these needs.

In addition to traditional forms of R&D support, universities and government labs should be encouraged to form more partnerships with industry to develop tools and techniques that will enhance everyday field applications. This will help effect the transition between the state of knowledge and the state of practice.

To ensure rapid technical transfer from research to practice, research could be carried out by teams that include both practitioners (e.g., geobiologists, geochemists, geophysicists) and clients (e.g., environmental scientists, civil engineers). Such research teams should communicate their results to the scientific, engineering, and user communities in widely available venues and in forms suitable for more immediate adoption.

AUTOMATION OF TECHNIQUES

Research and development efforts applied to automation of data acquisition, data processing, and decision making could produce rapid improvement in all aspects of near-surface characterization and should be given a high priority for research funding.

Automation can be applied to data acquisition (e.g., robotics), data processing, and decision making (e.g., use of expert systems and other decision tools for survey planning and data interpretation). The benefits of automation include ease of use, consistency, quality assurance, and cost reduction. It also could enable more rapid technology transfer of the latest tools and techniques from the research lab to the field, thus enabling the state of the practice to be nearer to the state of the science. Finally, automation could help the site characterization industry deal with periodic shortages of trained professionals in specialized fields.

At present, for example, there is a potential shortage of individuals with advanced education in shallow-exploration geophysics. Low enrollments in university programs for the past decade, coupled with employment opportunities in the oil and mining industries, may make it difficult for site characterization companies to hire enough qualified professionals. However, computers can help design a site survey, automate data acquisition, check the quality of data, process the data, model the data, and provide a rough interpretation. For example, the Geophysics Advisor Expert System (Olhoeft, 1992) can help select appropriate geophysical tools to apply to EPA Superfund site problems (and in the process, educate site managers and contractors). However, such systems are guides and will not replace the need for skilled professionals; the uniqueness of sites makes it difficult to include every possibility in such systems. Another example is a tunnel detection system (Olhoeft, 1993) that automatically tests data quality through 12 consistency tests (and, if necessary, indicates what might be wrong with the data and ways to correct them). The system also processes the data for the normal logistical, operational, and instrumental artifacts; manipulates and models the data; and provides a graphical output of the most likely location for detection of a tunnel. At each step, the program provides quantitative data processing, modeling, and interpretive (uncertainty and confidence) indicators. These types of automation and decision support systems can provide the expertise to complement the skills of practitioners and help alleviate personnel shortages.

Automation also can make an important contribution to work in hazardous environments. Not only can robotic technology make it possible to avoid putting humans in dangerous situations, but expert systems and decision support tools can further enhance the quality of data by making real-time decisions about optimizing acquisition parameters. Ultimately, such systems could improve data quality, lower cost, and enhance safety.

These are only a few examples of automation techniques that could provide expertise, guide the characterization process, and ensure quality control. The necessary capability to develop such techniques exists in universities and government laboratories, and the techniques could be rapidly embedded in systems for broad use. Impediments to broader development and use of these automated systems include the issue of deciding how such systems should be certified, who should be authorized to conduct the certification, and how the systems will be updated.

Automation will not replace skilled practitioners; however, it can significantly increase the knowledge base that practitioners use to accomplish their jobs. By producing a better result, more rapidly and at lower cost, robotics and decision support systems could be the key to more—and more effective—use of site characterization methods. Therefore, automation of site characterization processes should be pursued on two broad fronts simultaneously. Experts in universities and government laboratories should move aggressively to develop techniques and systems for automation of activities and decision-making processes. At the same time, the key regulatory bodies should develop certification policies and procedures using experts from the legal, technical, and political arenas. Research and development should include (but not be limited to) the following:

• Expert systems to provide advice and guidance in designing characterization surveys, optimizing parameters, estimating probability of success, validating decisions, and justifying costs;

- Automated data acquisition instruments to ensure competent use, enable field processing and interpretation, and provide quality control;
- Expert systems, decision trees, and pattern recognition software to guide data processing sequences;
- Decision support systems to assist in interpretation, incorporating effective use of modeling and simulation to validate possible interpretations and provide quantitative estimates of uncertainty;
- Policies and procedures for certifying the validity and effectiveness of automation tools; and
- Guidelines for regulatory adoption of the appropriate and proper use of certified automation tools.

MONITORING TEMPORAL VARIATIONS

Many site characterization problems involve changes with time. Examples include monitoring engineered barriers to confirm containment of contaminants, analyzing changes in soil moisture to assess water fluxes, or surveying an environmental remediation site to characterize the reduction in the extent of subsurface contamination. A single observation or survey at a characterization site may show the distribution of materials in question at that point in time, but it will not provide information about changes from earlier conditions or help predict future evolution.

In many cases, properly designed multiple surveys can detect and monitor small changes in properties with higher resolution than is possible within a single survey. Significant advances can result from the development of exploration strategies (using existing tools) for acquiring, processing, and interpreting time-varying information. In the long term, research also is needed to develop measurement technology that will allow monitoring new processes such as in situ leaching or bioremediation.

Uses for time-varying information include the following:

- The ability to predict changes that may occur in response to human activity (or lack thereof) is essential to design and defend remediation plans.
- Baseline data and historical information often are needed to assess liability or responsibility. Where baseline information does not exist, data from repeated measurements sometimes can be extrapolated backwards to provide insight into history.
- Monitoring the remediation process might either verify that the plan is working or provide a quantitative basis for changing the plan to improve the chances of success.

Observing contaminant transport in the subsurface has been done almost exclusively through the use of monitoring wells. However, certain situations may preclude the use of monitoring wells. Even where wells are allowed, they often may not be the most-cost effective solution, and in many cases they provide limited areal coverage. Noninvasive methods could provide an economical means for large-scale, long-term monitoring and also reveal the dynamics of subsurface processes; for example:

• Monitoring of the land surface by remote sensing techniques could provide much information about the subsurface conditions in the top meter or so.
• Changes in moisture conditions at the surface could indicate subsurface heterogeneity. Soil-gas surveys could monitor microbial activity or assess the success of remediation schemes.
• Repeat geophysical surveys could indicate changes in the distribution of subsurface fluids, which is particularly useful in monitoring contaminant movement (e.g., DNAPL remobilization) during site remediation activities.

Noninvasive monitoring for prolonged periods of time should be considered an integral part of site characterization, underground construction, and remediation projects that require monitoring.

Noninvasive techniques could augment traditional invasive monitoring and enhance our ability to test and develop an understanding of subsurface processes. In some cases, noninvasive methods are the only alternative. The following R&D efforts are needed for this to become common practice:

• Geological noise and other factors limit the resolution of a survey method. If the noise does not change with time, then changes in key properties often can be detected with higher resolution than the properties themselves can be mapped. The development of processing and interpretation techniques that take advantage of differential measurements would allow existing tools and survey methods to be used effectively for monitoring.
• As new remediation techniques are developed (in situ leaching, bioremediation, etc.), monitoring properties indicative of the progress of a remediative actions might be difficult using existing characterization tools and survey methods. Fundamentally new tools (such as magnetic resonance imaging and seismic-electric techniques) offer the promise of making measurements previously thought impossible. Monitoring needs for the next decade could require a long-term, sustained program of fundamental research into "exotic" measurement technologies.

PROPERTIES AND PROCESSES

Site characterization historically has focused on mapping the subsurface geometry (e.g., location of anomalies, shapes of boundaries). Physical, chemical, and biological properties and processes (including coupling between processes) are at least as important as geometry; however, there has been limited research into the noninvasive measurement of such properties and processes and their distribution. Developing the ability to observe these properties and processes noninvasively will require long-term research, from the perspective of both understanding the phenomena and developing the methodology to measure and interpret these phenomena.

Until recently, measurements of properties (e.g., the bearing strength of the foundation material at a construction site) usually have been done on samples obtained by drilling or other intrusive means. Today there is a growing demand for nonintrusive surveys that measure in situ properties (chemical and biological as well as mechanical). For example, no longer is it sufficient to find the top of the saturated zone; now it also is necessary to determine water quality or identify contaminants. In the future, solutions to environmental and engineering problems of the shallow subsurface also will depend on understanding and observing in situ chemical and biological processes and the interactions between them.

Characterization methods used to find anomalies or map subsurface geometry actually are detecting variations in properties or mapping boundaries between areas of different properties. However, quantitative relationships between the phenomena being observed and the values of the in situ properties usually are not well defined and often involve ambiguity. Therefore, although the location of the variations or boundaries can be mapped, relatively little information about the properties themselves (such as the specific contaminant being mapped) can be determined. The problem is worse if the target involves a chemical or biological process because, in many cases there is little knowledge about the relationship between the in situ process and the phenomena observable at the surface. An example would be the situation wherein a biological agent was introduced into a region containing a chemical pollutant. We know little about whether the biological process produces any effect that is potentially measurable, let alone how to measure it.

> *As part of a basic research program, there needs to be a significant effort directed toward quantification of physical and chemical realities of what is being sensed as well as possible interactions between in situ properties and processes.*

Some noninvasive methods for subsurface characterization are well understood. For instance, there is a good correlation between seismic measurements and the elastic properties of the material being sensed. This is not the case for many other measurements. Fundamental studies should be initiated and expanded to include the following:

• Understand subsurface processes and the interactions between them, and identify the measurable properties that might be associated with these processes or combinations of processes.

• Establish theoretical and phenomenological relationships between the properties and processes of interest and the phenomena that could be measured noninvasively at the surface.

• Develop instruments and techniques that will allow these phenomena to be measured with useful resolution and adequate signal-to-noise ratio.

• Produce the interpretive tools and procedures to invert the surface measurements into an accurate description of the properties or processes at depth.

Fundamental studies should be supplemented by variable-scale testing, ranging from laboratory examination of cores to full-scale integrated surveys of standard test sites. The National Geotechnical Test Site Program, supported by the National Science Foundation and the Federal Highway Administration and managed by the National Council for Geo-Engineering and Construction, might serve as a useful model. Other test sites (e.g., those at the University of Arizona, Stanford University, and the Idaho National Environmental Engineering Laboratory) have been established for specific research projects. These test sites can be used to develop new techniques and to validate models.

OPPORTUNITIES FOR INNOVATIVE MEASUREMENTS

Most existing technologies measure physical phenomena and are used to interpret physical properties and processes. Few methods exist to monitor the chemical or biological properties and processes that are becoming increasingly important, particularly in areas such as groundwater management and hazardous waste mitigation. The discovery of fundamentally new measurement technologies, the ability to observe fundamentally new phenomena, and better interaction between disciplines are essential for nonintrusive site characterization to meet current and future needs.

Nonintrusive characterization methods inherently rely on "action at a distance." Furthermore, the action at a distance must occur rapidly compared to the time scale of the process in order for the measurement to reflect current conditions. For example, biological agents working on organic pollutants at depth might produce a volatile by-product that can migrate to the surface where it could be mapped with a soil-gas survey. However, if the rate of propagation of the volatile product is slower than the action of the biological agent, the soil-gas survey could be describing conditions that have changed by the time of the survey.

The measurement of physical phenomena on the surface to infer physical properties at depth is relatively well developed. However, many of the challenges in site characterization for environmental applications involve interpreting surface measurements to infer chemical and biological properties and processes at depth. Methods for accomplishing the latter are not as well developed, and in many cases, there are no quantitative measurements that can yield information about such properties or processes.

Some physical phenomena can be interpreted to yield such information (for example, subtle features in a ground penetrating radar signal are linked to the chemistry of certain subsurface pollutants); however the relationships between the phenomena and the properties or processes generally are not well understood. There are a few geochemical measurements that also can provide information about in situ properties (the use of "sniffers" to sample gases emanating from the soil), but again the connection between the source and the observation is not always well understood. Furthermore, in many cases involving geochemical measurements, the time scale of the phenomenon is long relative to the process being monitored (e.g., the soil-gas survey mentioned above), in which case the measurements may be of little practical use.

In the future, the committee expects subsurface biological activity to become a major issue; however, the ability to relate surface observations to biological properties and processes is even more limited. A few physical measurements indirectly involve biological agents (for example, spectral imaging can be used to interpret the health of plants that, in turn, can indicate depth to water table). However, there are few, if any, ways to infer biological agents or activity at depth directly from physical observations on the surface. It may be possible to use geochemical observations to infer geobiological properties or processes, but at the present time the capabilities of most of these methods are limited and their efficacy has not been demonstrated. Such measurements also are subject to the time-delay problems mentioned above.

The committee believes that the lack of progress in these areas is the result of insufficient research directed to the connections between the physical phenomena and the chemical or biological property or process; part of this is probably a lack of understanding or appreciation of the importance of these problems. However, the problem may be more deeply rooted in the lack of communication between geophysicists, geochemists, and geobiologists. Fragmentation in the traditional earth sciences is well documented (there are 32 separate professional societies that are members of the American Geological Institute and even more that do not participate in this organization), but the gap between fields and geochemistry or (especially) geobiology is even greater. Therefore, any increase in support for research in mapping chemical or biological properties must be accompanied by a commitment to truly effective cross-disciplinary interaction.

Long-term research to develop fundamentally new noninvasive tools and techniques should be given a high priority, with emphasis on research done by multidisciplinary teams.

Among the challenges in site characterization technologies in the coming decades will be measurement, both direct and indirect, of geochemical and